WILD CREATURES IN WINTER

Old Homestead Tales Series

Wild

CREATURES

in Winter

by NEIL WAYNE NORTHEY

Drawings by William Wilke

ORGINALLY PUBLISHED BY:
PACIFIC PRESS PUBLISHING
BOISE, ID
RE-PUBLISHED BY:
A.B. PUBLISHING
ITHACA, MI
COVER ART AND DESIGN BY:
JAMES CONVERSE
COPYRIGHT 1998

Contents

Introduction

DID you ever stand by the window on a Wintry Day, watching the Merry Little Snowflakes come dancing down, and wonder what all the Wild Creatures were doing? To be sure you have, unless you live in a country where the Fleecy Snow never falls.

When this earth was first created, there was no such thing as Fleecy Snow upon it. God never intended that Old Man Winter should freeze the Dancing Little Leaflets and make them fall. There was not even rain upon the earth until the time of the Flood. But when sin entered the world, there were many, many changes.

At creation the weather was neither too cold nor too hot. It was exactly right to please every living thing. The Feathered Friends did not have to fly away in search of a warmer place to live, as many of them do now each fall. And the Furry Friends lived the same the year round.

But how different it is now! Even Fearful the Man has had to change his manner of living to meet the changed conditions. Every place we go in the Great Wide World we see people who are living differently from the way they do in other places.

So it is with the Wild Creatures. They have learned how to live under the changed conditions in this sinful world, which are so different from what they were in the Garden of Eden.

In this, the last of *Old Homestead Tales,* you will read about what the Wild Creatures do in Wintry Weather on the Old Homestead. Perhaps it will tell you some of the things you were wondering about as you stood by the window and watched the Merry Little Snowflakes come dancing down.   THE AUTHOR.

Denver, Colorado.

CHAPTER 1

Jack Frost Appears

IT was a cool night in September when Jack Frost first stole out with his paintbrush and began to paint all the Dancing Little Leaflets on the Old Homestead beautiful colors. Yes, sir; it was a cool night. Jack Frost was the son of Old Man Winter, and whenever Jack began to paint the Quaking Aspen Trees a bright yellow, and the Oaks brown and red, and the Maples gold and red, everyone knew that Old Man Winter was not far away. You should have seen the beautiful scarlet color he painted the Twining Vines that had crept up the side of the Grand Old House.

It seemed as if when Jack Frost once got started to coloring around the Old Homestead, he never knew when to stop. He daubed the Dancing Little Leaflets in the Apple Orchard a bright lemon; and how pretty they were beside the Flaming Red Apples! Then he went down along Little River, which flowed through the Wide-Wide Pasture and the Green Meadow, and touched first a Drooping Willow Tree here and then a patch of Blackberry Brambles there, and then he stopped in the Rustling Cornfield long enough to turn it into a fashionable tan color.

After that Jack Frost went to work in the Black Forest, and he daubed right and left with his paintbrush. In a little while you never would have known it was the same Black Forest if it had not been for all the Great Pine Trees and Blue Spruce Trees. Of course he could not paint them, for they were green all winter.

How busy everyone became when Jack Frost first hinted that Old Man Winter would soon arrive! Early morning Mr. Smith was out bright and early cutting the Rustling Corn and making it into Rustling Corn Shocks. There were Golden Pumpkins to be gathered, and Flaming Red Apples to be picked, and Juicy Tomatoes to be canned. And there were carrots and turnips and potatoes to be dug and stored away in the Dark Root Cellar.

It certainly was a busy time for Mr. Smith and Mrs. Smith and Bud and Mary, harvesting all the crops and vegetables before Old Man Winter came and froze them. In a little while that Dark Root Cellar was filled to the top with all kinds of good things to be eaten during the Cold-Cold Days when the garden would be covered with snow.

After that there was much wood to be cut and

hauled to the Woodshed for the Glowing Fireplace and the Shining Kitchen Stove.

But the Smiths were not the only ones who
were busy on the Old Homestead. I should say
not! You should have seen how busy the Furry
Friends and Feathered Friends were. All some of
the Feathered Friends had to do was to spread
their wings and fly away to their winter homes in
the Sunny Southland when Old Man Winter
came too near. Some of them, like Spink the Bob-
olink, did not even wait for Jack Frost to come,
but left the Old Homestead not long after their
babies were strong enough to fly that far.

You see, not all the Feathered Friends enjoyed
traveling the same way any more than all people
do. Some of them, like Spink, wanted to start early

The Mallards
were about the last
to leave for the
Sunny Southland.

and not fly so far all at once. Spink went part way, and then stopped to eat rice and grow fat before he finished his journey. But some of the Feathered Friends, like the Bluebirds and the Mallards and Honker the Goose, waited until the very last minute almost, before they left for the Sunny Southland. But Honker and the Mallards were about the last to leave, and then how fast they did fly!

Some of the Feathered Friends liked to fly at night, while others flew mostly during the day. Then they could stop and find good things to eat as they went along. Wouldn't you think that they would get very, very tired flying so far? But there was Flash the Hummingbird, who was the tiniest of all of them, and he flew right across the Gulf of Mexico! Who would imagine that one as small as he could fly more than five hundred miles in one night, and that across water!

But there were many Feathered Friends who lived on the Old Homestead and in the Black Forest all the year. They were not afaid of Old Man Winter. And, of course, the Furry Friends did not leave, because they could not fly. So when Jack Frost arrived at the Old Homestead with his Paint Pots, the Wild Creatures that did not leave had much to do.

Every day the Laughing Yellow Sun had

Pesty the Magpie stayed through the winter.

moved just a little farther southward. Shorter and shorter grew the days, and colder and colder were the nights.

"Look at the ice on the water tank!" said Bud to Mary, as they left for school one morning.

"Yes, I suppose the last of the Feathered Friends will soon be leaving for the Sunny Southland. Jim Crow and his cousins Tattler the Jay and Pesty the Magpie will not leave, and neither will Dandy the Chickadee nor his cousin White-breast the Nuthatch nor Downy the Wood-pecker."

"And Bobby White and Ringneck the Pheasant and Drummer the Grouse and Hungarian the Partridge would not think of leaving the Old Homestead," said Bud.

(13)

"Sometimes I wish that I could fly away to the Sunny Southland for a while like Robin Red and Jenny Wren and some of the other Feathered Friends," said Mary. "But then I would not want to miss all the fun of skating, and coasting, and sitting by the Broad Hearth on Wintry Nights."

"Yes, and think how much fun it is to play Fox and Geese in the Fleecy Snow!" said Bud. "Whatever *would* we do if we lived where there was never any Fleecy Snow?"

CHAPTER 2

Paddletail the Beaver Goes to Work

"I BELIEVE it is time for us to start to fill our Pantry before Old Man Winter freezes our Wildwood Pond," said Paddletail the Beaver one evening.

"Yes, it is time," said Mrs. Paddletail, "for soon the Secluded Ditches and the Wildwood Pond will be covered with Glassy Ice, and then we cannot swim to the Broad Flat after Tender Buds and Spicy Bark. We had better begin to fill our Pantry at once."

Paddletail the Beaver and Mrs. Paddletail and Brownie and Silver Paddletail lived in a Hidden Den in a bank of their Wildwood Pond, which was in the Black Forest. Once upon a time Paddletail had built a High Dam across Little River, where it flowed through the Black Forest; and the High Dam had made a Wildwood Pond for the Paddletails. In it they could swim, and play Dive and Spin and Water Tag.

At first the Paddletails had lived in a Hidden Den in the bank, with a Secret Doorway under water. Then they built a Brushy House, with a

Secret Doorway like the one at the Hidden Den. In it they had lived all summer.

One day late in the summer Paddletail and Mrs. Paddletail had taken Brownie and Silver on a long excursion. They had gone away up Little River, and had expected to trade houses with Flattail the Beaver and his family. That seems like a strange thing; but that was what beavers sometimes did.

The Paddletails had given their Brushy House to the Flattails and had gone to live in the Flattail's Brushy House farther up Little River. But when the Paddletails found it, there was another family of beavers already living there. So the Paddletails had returned to their own Wildwood

Paddletail cut down a Giant Cottonwood Tree, and over it fell, kersplash!

Pond. Naturally, they could not live in their Brushy House after giving it to the Flattails, so they lived in their Old Hidden Den in the Clay Bank until they could build another Brushy House.

What Paddletail expected to do was someday to build another Brushy House right beside the one he had given to the Flattails, and then they could build a roof over both houses and make a Big Colony House.

When Paddletail the Beaver and his family returned to their Wildwood Pond, Jack Frost had already been there and had painted the Quaking Aspen Grove, and the Drooping Willow Trees, and the Soft Poplar Trees many pretty colors. Paddletail knew that he did not have time to build another Brushy House and also to gather a supply of good things to eat during Cold-Cold Days before Old Man Winter would come. He decided he would fill his Pantry, and then, when Jolly Spring came back again, he would build his Brushy House. The Hidden Den would be a nice warm place in which to live till then.

So while Bud and Mary Smith were carrying Flaming Red Apples and Golden Pumpkins and other good things into their Dark Root Cellar to last them during the Wintry Weather, there were

Paddletail and Mrs. Paddletail and Brownie and Silver filling their Pantry.

But what a queer Pantry they had! In case you do not know where Paddletail's Pantry was, I will tell you. It was deep, deep under water, and not far from his Secret Doorway. Yes, that is where Paddletail the Beaver stored his food for winter. Then whenever he wanted something to eat after the Glassy Ice covered his Wildwood Pond and he could no longer cut down Soft Poplar Trees, all he had to do was to dive down through his Secret Doorway, and there he was right in his Pantry.

Now what do you suppose Paddletail put in his Pantry to eat during the Cold-Cold Days? He filled it with Green Twigs and Willowy Poles and Stubby Sticks and Little Logs.

First, he cut down a Giant Cottonwood Tree, and over it fell, kersplash! right into the Wildwood Pond, by his Hidden Den. There were many, many Green Twigs and much Spicy Bark on the Springy Limbs that were under the water. There was enough to last Paddletail and his family many days. But that was not the only thing that Paddletail wanted of the Giant Cottonwood. No, sir; that was not all. The Giant Cottonwood Tree was to be Paddletail's Pantry.

You see, if Paddletail had brought his Green

Twigs and Willowy Poles and Stubby Sticks and Little Logs and left them in the water near his Secret Doorway, soon they would have floated away; and then he would have had nothing to eat during the Wintry Weather. But Paddletail was wise, and whenever he brought a load to his Pantry, he fastened it under the Springy Limbs of the Giant Cottonwood Tree far down where the Glassy Ice would not reach.

Sometimes Paddletail held his Green Twigs on the bottom of his Wildwood Pond by piling Oozy Mud on them. Sometimes he would hold them down with a rock. And so it was that as the nights grew colder and colder, Paddletail's Pantry became fuller and fuller.

Now, I suppose you will wonder how Paddletail could eat his meals under water. He did not mind that at all. Sometimes he could carry Green Twigs into his Hidden Den and eat them. And sometimes the water in the Wildwood Pond went down some and left an air space under the Glassy Ice. But then Paddletail could easily stay under water more than ten minutes if he had to.

That is the way Paddletail filled his Pantry when Jack Frost told him that Old Man Winter was on his way from the Land of Ice.

CHAPTER 3

Danny Muskrat Repairs His House

"I SEE that Paddletail the Beaver is filling his Pantry," said Danny Muskrat to Mrs. Muskrat.

"Yes, and it is about time for us to go to work ourselves," said Mrs. Muskrat. "We must make our house warmer before Old Man Winter arrives."

The Muskrats lived in a Grassy House on the Wildwood Pond not far from Paddletail the Beaver's Hidden Den. The Beavers and the Muskrats were good friends. Almost every night the

The Muskrats lived in a Grassy House not far from Paddletail's Hidden Den.

Muskrats would go to visit the Beavers for a game of Water Tag.

Now it happened that when Jack Frost came to the Old Homestead, the first ones who noticed him were the Furry Folk who lived in the water much of the time. You see, as soon as Danny Muskrat and the other Water Animals left the water on Cold-Cold Nights the Playful Air Whiffs began to freeze Sharp Little Icicles on their fur. So, as the nights grew colder and colder, they had to stay in the water more and more to keep the Sharp Little Icicles from forming on their fur. Danny Muskrat knew that after the Wildwood Pond was covered with Glassy Ice, the only place he could go out of water was in his Grassy House.

During the Balmy Summer Days, Danny liked to sit on his Grassy House, or on a Floating Log, or at a Mud Slide, while he ate his Sweet Cattail Stalks and Juicy Water Bulbs. But after the Wintry Weather came, Danny knew he would have to eat them in his Grassy House, or under the Glassy Ice if he could find a place. So his Grassy House had to be warm.

Away went Danny and Mrs. Muskrat, and soon they were carrying large bunches of Tumbled Bulrushes and Green Water Moss and Fuzzy Cattail Heads and Swamp Grass, and piling it on their

Grassy House. It was no trouble at all to find plenty of things with which to make their house warmer, and within a few nights their Grassy House had thick, warm sides.

Danny Muskrat was better off than Paddletail the Beaver in one way. He did not have to fill a Pantry. That was because the Juicy Water Bulbs and Sweet Cattail Stalks grew under water. At least there were enough under water so that Danny could usually find plenty under the Glassy Ice. But Danny had a dining room in his Grassy House, and sometimes he kept some Juicy Water Bulbs there so he would have a supply in very cold weather. He did not always eat all that he carried into his Grassy House for supper; then he would have some left for another day.

Now, it was a wonder how Danny could swim around under the Glassy Ice and find something to eat without drowning; but he did. Yes, sir; he could go as far as he wanted to. When Danny left his Grassy House, he took a full breath of air. After he had swum a long way and needed a fresh breath, if he could not find an air space under the ice, he let out his breath against the ice; then soon it was fresh and ready to be breathed again. That was a trick that Paddletail knew also.

But there was one who lived at the Wildwood

Pond that could do more than either Paddletail or Danny. That was Croaker the Frog.

"Cronk, cronk," he said, one Cold-Cold Day; "I believe it is time to get ready for winter."

Then all Croaker did was to burrow down deep into the Oozy Mud in the bottom of the Wildwood Pond and go to sleep. There he stayed until Jolly Spring came back and awoke him. Wasn't that an unusual way to spend the winter?

Then there was Ouzel the Dipper, who lived near Paddletail's High Dam, where the Swift Waterfall came tumbling over. You would never see Ouzel worrying about Cold-Cold Days. He wore a coat of Soft Warm Down, and he could dive right through the Swift Waterfall or into the Icy Water and not mind it at all, though what he could find there to eat is a mystery.

"Cronk, cronk," said Croaker the Frog. "It is time to get ready for winter."

One would never have guessed that Ouzel liked to play in the water any more than he would have thought that Jenny Wren did, because he was not much larger than Jenny Wren and looked somewhat like her. But while Jenny Wren was playing in the Sunny Southland, there was Ouzel sitting on a rock and looking into the Icy Water for something to dive in after.

Each day after Jack Frost came, and even before he came, the Feathered Friends around the Wildwood Pond became scarcer and scarcer. Crooner the Dove left his nest in the Giant Cottonwood Tree near Dandy the Chickadee's nest, and went out to the Yellow Stubble Field to live for a while where he could eat the scattered Tempting Kernels.

Browny Thrasher and Mew-Mew the Catbird left the Big Jungle Thicket and started for the Land of Sunshine. Alcyon the Kingfisher had to leave also when the Glassy Ice would not let him catch fish any more. Even Pesty the Magpie spent more time away from the Black Forest.

"It seems as if everyone is leaving," said Danny Muskrat.

"Yes, it *is* rather quiet around here," said Paddletail the Beaver.

"Tap-tap-tap-tap," went Redhead the Woodpecker on a Giant Cottonwood Tree; "I am still here, and I haven't quite made up my mind to leave."

It seemed as if Redhead never could decide whether to go south or not until the last minute; and then he was as likely to stay as to go. You see, he could usually find plenty of Tree Borers and such things to eat all winter; so it really did not make much difference to him.

CHAPTER 4

Snowshoe the Hare Changes Coats

"HOE-HOE-HOE," said Great Horn the Owl; "It must be time to get up." And then he blinked his large, round eyes a few times to make sure he was awake.

Great Horn had been sleeping all day in the Heavy Boughs of a Great Pine Tree. He liked to hide and sleep during the day because he could not see well then. But when the Long Shadows began to chase one another through the Black Forest, Great Horn was ready to start his night's hunt, for then he could see better.

Great Horn left his Heavy Bough and flew silently to a High Limb of an Old Hollow Stub, to look around.

"Hoe-hoe-hoe," he said, "Jack Frost has caused many of the Dancing Little Leaflets to fall off, and I can see through the Rabbit Bushes and the Bitter Willow Bushes so much better. I believe I will fly over to Little River and see if I can find Snowshoe the Hare or Jimmy the Swamp Rabbit. I surely would like tender rabbit for breakfast."

You see, Great Horn the Owl ate his breakfast

"Hoe-Hoe-Hoe," said Great Horn the Owl.
"It must be time to get up."

in the evening instead of in the morning, because he slept all day and hunted at night.

Away flew Great Horn as silently as a shadow through the Black Tree Tops. "Hoe-hoe-hoe," he said; "I wonder if Snowshoe the Hare is still living in his Bitter Willow Thicket over by Paddletail's Wildwood Pond."

Snowshoe's Bitter Willow Thicket was along Little River just above the place where Little River flowed into the Wildwood Pond. Great Horn had been there many times, and he knew every Lookout Stub and High Limb along the way. Every little while he would stop and look around to see if there were any Frolicking Bunnies in sight.

Now it happened that when Jack Frost nipped

the Dancing Little Leaflets, almost the first trees to undress for their long winter's sleep were the Bitter Willow Trees in the Thicket where Snowshoe the Hare lived. Yes, sir; in a little while there was scarcely a Dancing Little Leaflet left on them.

You may be sure that when the Dancing Little Leaflets began to fall off, Snowshoe the Hare was worried. You see, Snowshoe lived in a Cozy Form, which was like a little round nest on the ground, and he knew that when all the Dancing Little Leaflets had fallen there would not be much to hide his Cozy Form. No, sir; it would be in plain sight of Great Horn the Owl and Shadow the Lynx and anyone else that came along.

"Oh, dear me," said Snowshoe, when he saw the Dancing Little Leaflets come tumbling down; "I fear that I shall be caught if I stay here."

So Snowshoe the Hare decided to move over into the Big Jungle Thicket for a while. There were many, many Blackberry Brambles and Twining Vines and Dead Grasses in which he could hide. That was why Snowshoe was not in his Bitter Willow Thicket when Great Horn the Owl came to look for him.

But there was one Great Enemy that Snowshoe feared, even in the seclusion of the Big Jungle

Thicket, and that was Shadow the Lynx. Snowshoe feared that Shadow would come sneaking noiselessly through the Big Jungle Thicket on his large, padded feet and pounce upon him before he saw him. It really was hard to see anyone coming among all those Blackberry Brambles and Twining Vines, and no one could hear Shadow when he walked.

It is a wonder that Snowshoe did not find a Friendly Burrow into which he could run when he wanted to hide, as Peter and Molly Cottontail did. But Snowshoe was like his big cousin Jack the Jumper. He did not like to live in a Friendly Burrow. Neither did Jimmy the Swamp Rabbit.

Jack the Jumper really did not need a Friendly Burrow. He lived on the Broad Prairie and in the

Snowshoe the Hare had a new white coat instead of his dusky brown one.

Rustling Cornfield; and whenever he saw Ranger the Coyote or some other Enemy coming near, he jumped out of his Cozy Form and ran away.

And how Jack could run!

Jimmy the Swamp Rabbit did not need a Friendly Burrow, because he could jump into the Singing Water and swim away from his Furry Enemies; that is, he could when the Singing Water was not frozen.

Now although Snowshoe the Hare could not run nearly so fast and so far as his cousin Jack the Jumper, or swim like his other cousin Jimmy the Swamp Rabbit, there was one thing he could do that neither Jack nor Jimmy could do. That was to change the color of his coat.

Of course Snowshoe really was not the one that did the changing. It was the work of God, who created Snowshoe in the beginning. You see, during the summer months while there were all kinds of Bushes and Grasses and Vines in which Snowshoe could hide, the Lord gave him a dusky brown coat to wear so that Great Horn the Owl and Shadow the Lynx and Shaggy the Wolf and Terror the Hunter could not see him so easily when he was sitting in his Cozy Form.

But when Old Man Winter came and covered the Great Wide World with Fleecy Snow, the

Lord knew that anyone could see Snowshoe as plain as day if he were sleeping on the Soft White Blanket in his dusky brown coat. So He gave him a new white coat each fall, about the time that the Bluebirds were leaving for the Sunny Southland. And then Snowshoe could go back to his Bitter Willow Thicket to live.

CHAPTER 5

Worker the Gray Squirrel Visits Johnny Chuck

"LISTEN to the noise that Chatterer the Red Squirrel is making!" said Worker the Gray Squirrel to himself. "I wonder whom he is scolding this morning."

The reason Chatterer was making such a fuss was that when he awoke that morning and peeped out from his Hollow Den Tree in the Wide-Wide Pasture, he saw that Jack Frost had visited there during the night. Yes, sir; everything was covered with Pretty White Crystals right up to Chatterer's doorstep.

Now Chatterer knew that when the Pretty White Crystals appeared it was time for him to fill his Secret Storehouses with Tempting Kernels and Delicious Pine Cones and Sweet Acorns before Old Man Winter hid all of them under a Soft White Blanket. Chatterer already had many, many Dried Mushrooms hidden away; but that would not be enough to last him during the Wintry Weather.

Down through the Wood Lot he went, trying

to see what he could find, and scolding everyone he met. He surely was a noisy fellow.

Worker the Gray Squirrel lived in a Big Stick Nest in the top of a tree not far from Chatterer's Hollow Den Tree.

"I believe I will watch Chatterer and see that he does not rob one of my Secret Storehouses," said Worker.

You see, Worker had been busy quite a while gathering all kinds of Goodies and hiding them away so he would have something to eat during the Cold-Cold Days.

But Chatterer did not like to work so well as Worker did. He would rather spend his time looking for something to steal. In the summer he looked for Round Little Nests from which to steal eggs. Then in the fall, when he should have been gathering things to put into his Secret Storehouses, he spent part of his time hunting for Worker's Secret Storehouses so that he could steal from them. That was why Worker decided to watch Chatterer.

Down through the Wood Lot scampered Chatterer, and then across the Wide-Wide Pasture toward the Green Meadow. And there was Worker the Gray Squirrel following him not far behind.

At last Worker decided that Chatterer had

Chatterer the Red Squirrel peeped
out of his Hollow Den Tree.

given up looking for his Secret Storehouses. So
Worker thought he would go over on the side of
High Cliff and see if he could find some Brown
Hazelnuts on the Hazelnut Brush that grew there.

Now it is a mystery how Worker ever expected
to find half of his Secret Storehouses, for he had
hidden things away under logs and in hollow trees
and in knots. Sometimes he had even dug a Little
Hole in the ground and covered up two or three
Sweet Acorns. But if you had been there when
Worker was ready to eat them, you would have
seen him dig down into the Fleecy Snow right
where they were.

Worker was afraid to hide all his Goodies in one
Secret Storehouse, because he knew that if Chat-

(34)

terer found it, he would have nothing left. Worker thought that he might find some Brown Hazelnuts on the side of High Cliff, and then he could tuck some under rocks for a feast on a Cold-Cold Day.

Sure enough, Worker found a patch of Hazelnut Brush, and there were many nuts hanging there. Worker had found them barely in time, for in a few days Bud and Mary Smith would be along gathering nuts to eat during the Wintry Weather. Of course Bud and Mary did not care if Worker took some of the Brown Hazelnuts, for he really had as much right to them as they had.

Soon he was busy cutting off Brown Hazelnuts and dropping them on the ground. Then he expected to gather them up and hide them.

"Kerplunk!" went a Brown Hazelnut; and

"Oh, no," said Johnny Chuck; "I never bother to fill a Secret Storehouse."

where do you suppose it landed? Why, right on Johnny Chuck's head.

You see, Johnny Chuck lived in a Friendly Burrow under a large, flat rock right under that Hazelnut Brush. Johnny Chuck had been lying on that rock sound asleep, while the Bright Little Sunbeams warmed his broad back. You should have seen Johnny Chuck jump when that Brown Hazelnut dropped on his head.

"Ouch!" he cried; "I surely thought Aquila the Golden Eagle had grabbed me."

"I didn't see you," said Worker the Gray Squirrel. "But why are you sleeping on such a fine day? Are you not ready to fill your Secret Storehouse for the Wintry Weather?"

"Oh, no," said Johnny Chuck; "I never bother to fill a Secret Storehouse."

"But what do you eat on the Cold-Cold Days, when everything is covered with Fleecy Snow?" asked Worker.

Johnny Chuck yawned. He was getting very, very sleepy. He was so sleepy he could scarcely hold his eyes open.

"Oh, I would rather sleep than eat," he said. "I believe I will go to bed right now." And down into his Friendly Burrow went Johnny Chuck.

In the fall while Chatterer and Worker are filling their Secret Storehouses, Johnny Chuck eats and eats and grows fatter and fatter. Then when the Chilly Fall Days come, down into his Friendly Burrow he goes, and there he curls up and goes sound asleep. Would you believe it, Johnny Chuck sometimes sleeps five months before he awakens! Yes, sir; he does not know when the Fleecy Snow is falling or anything.

Some people say that Johnny Chuck always awakens and comes out of his Friendly Burrow on February 2; and that if he sees his shadow, he goes back to bed again. They call it Groundhog Day. Of course that is a joke, because Johnny Chuck gets up when he feels like it, and he doesn't look for his shadow, either. What he looks for is something to eat; for he is very hungry after sleeping so long. I think I would be, too; wouldn't you?

CHAPTER 6

The Home of Tiny the Meadow Mouse

TINY the Meadow Mouse poked his head out of his Grassy Nest and looked around. He was looking to see if there were any Enemies waiting to pounce upon him. It seemed as if no one had so many Enemies as Tiny had. There were Feathered Enemies and Furry Enemies. Some were large and some were small. Everyone from Growler the Bear to Snoop the Weasel, and from Great Horn the Owl to Butcher the Shrike was always ready to catch Tiny and his friends. So

Tiny the Meadow Mouse poked his head out of his Grassy Nest and looked around.

Tiny had to be careful whenever he went any-where.

Now the reason why Tiny was leaving his Grassy Nest was that he expected to build another. He knew that Old Man Winter would soon arrive with his load of Fleecy Snow, and Tiny had to build a better home in which to live.

If Tiny had been like Tawny Chipmunk, he could have curled up in a Friendly Burrow under a rock somewhere and gone to sleep. But he wasn't like Tawny; so he needed a winter home. Tiny rather liked to run around in the Fleecy Snow and make many Secret Tunnels in it; but he liked a nice Soft Little Nest in which to stay when he was home. And Tiny thought it was time to build his Winter Home.

When Tiny peeped out of his Grassy Nest, he could not see any of his Enemies around. He felt quite sure it would be all right to start. Tiny wanted to find a place to build his Winter Home where there would be plenty of Goodies to eat near by.

Out hopped Tiny, and away he ran toward a Large Leaf that he saw not far away. Then under the Large Leaf he dived until he could get his breath and make sure that no one had seen him.

When Tiny looked out from under the Large

Tiny ran under the bark just in time to escape
Saw-Whet the Owl's sharp claws.

Leaf, everything seemed as safe as before. Not far away was a large piece of bark. Tiny decided it would be another good Resting Place. So out he jumped and ran toward it.

Suddenly there was a Swift Shadow, and Tiny ran under the bark just in time to escape Saw-Whet the Owl's sharp claws.

"Oh, dear, that was a narrow escape!" said Tiny. "I must be more careful."

Tiny did not leave the shelter of the bark until he was sure that Saw-Whet had left. And he never ran far between Resting Places.

At last Tiny came to the edge of a field. He sat under a Big Tumbleweed and listened.

"I do believe I hear Rustling Corn Shocks," said Tiny to himself.

Soon the Playful Air Whiffs blew merrily by, shaking down Dancing Little Leaflets from the Broad Oak that stood at the edge of the field. Over in the field the Rustling Corn Shocks made scraping noises as the Playful Air Whiffs rubbed the Dry Cornstalks together.

"Yes, sir, I do hear Rustling Corn Shocks," said Tiny. "I am going right over there and start to make my Soft Little Nest."

But there was one thing that worried Tiny the Meadow Mouse, and that was how to get over to the Rustling Corn Shocks without one of his Enemies seeing him. You see, it was quite a way over to the first Rustling Corn Shock. At least it was quite a way for Tiny. It must have been more than a mouse mile. After Mr. Smith had cut the Rustling Corn and made it into Rustling Corn Shocks, there were not many Hiding Places left.

"I wonder how I can get over to that Rustling Corn Shock," thought Tiny. It was quite a problem to know what to do.

Suddenly the Playful Air Whiffs came dancing across the ground at a merry rate. They acted as if they were going to a party and were hurrying to get there. Of course when they came to the Big Tumbleweed under which Tiny was hiding, they rolled it right over. And there was Tiny without anything over him. You should have seen Tiny run to the Big Tumbleweed and dive under it when it stopped.

Soon more Playful Air Whiffs came along and turned the Big Tumbleweed over again, and then Tiny had to run after it as he had before.

After that came more and more Playful Air Whiffs and rolled the Big Tumbleweed along, until Tiny was almost run down. And then, when Tiny was all out of breath from following after the Big Tumbleweed, away it flew so fast that poor Tiny could not begin to keep up.

"Oh, dear! oh, dear!" said Tiny; "what shall I do now?"

Then, what do you think? Well, right there by Tiny was a Rustling Corn Shock. The Big Tumbleweed had taken him right to it. My, but Tiny was glad to see it! He dived headfirst into a Narrow Doorway between two bundles of corn, and he didn't stop until he was clear in the middle of the Rustling Corn Shock. Then the first thing Tiny did was to sit down and nibble some of the Tempting Kernels.

"This place suits me exactly," he said to himself. "I will dig a Friendly Burrow into the Soft Warm Ground under the Rustling Corn Shock, and then I will make a Soft Little Nest in it."

Tiny liked to build his Soft Little Nest in a Friendly Burrow, because then if Farmer Smith took away the Rustling Corn Shock, Tiny would still have a home. And, besides, the Friendly Burrow would be much warmer.

Soon Tiny was busy making his Friendly Burrow, and when it was finished he gathered Hairy Corn Silks with which to make his Soft Little Nest. You see, instead of filling a Pantry with Favorite Food as Paddletail the Beaver did, or filling Secret Storehouses as Worker the Gray Squirrel did, Tiny found a Pantry that was already filled, and then he built his Winter Home by it.

CHAPTER 7

"Old Man Winter Is Coming"

ONE cold day in late fall a new visitor came to the Old Homestead. He was very small, and he wore a jaunty red cap on his head. His name was Timid the Kinglet. Almost the first thing he said was: "Old Man Winter is coming."

Everyone on the Old Homestead knew that already, for Jack Frost had said so; but Timid the Kinglet knew it even better than the others. The reason was that he had been living in the Chilly Northland, so he knew when Old Man Winter started south. Timid knew that soon it would be too stormy for him to stay in the Chilly Northland, and he had come to the Old Homestead to live during the Cold-Cold Days.

But Timid was not the only Feathered Friend that lived in the Chilly Northland and visited the Old Homestead in winter. There was Loxia the Crossbill and Snowy the Bunting and Junco the Snowbird and Bohemian the Waxwing and Butcher the Shrike and others. When the weather was too cold in the Land of Cold Breezes, they came to the Old Homestead to live until Jolly

Spring came and drove Old Man Winter back to his own land.

Timid the Kinglet liked the Old Homestead so well that sometimes he visited there during the summer. But you never would have known he was around, because he was so timid. He hid among the Shady Trees where he would not be seen.

Over by the Duck Pond, while Timid was hunting for Crawly Bugs to eat, he met Killdeer the Plover.

"Old Man Winter is coming," said Timid, but Killdeer did not seem to be much interested.

"Killdeer, killdeer," was all he said, which was his way of saying that he was not in any hurry to start for the Sunny Southland.

Sometimes it was the middle of winter before Killdeer really made up his mind to go; and even then he was as likely to stay as to go if the weather was not too cold.

"I wonder if there are any Crawly Bugs in the Black Forest," thought Timid; and away he flew to see if he could find some.

Now it happened that Dandy the Chickadee was also looking for Crawly Bugs and Tree Borers; and when Timid arrived at the Black Forest, there was Dandy hanging from the bottom side of a limb to see if there was anything hiding there. Of course, Timid did not think that was anything unusual, for he could do that himself.

"Old Man Winter is coming," said Timid.

"Yes, I know he is," said Dandy; "but that makes no difference to me. I expect to stay right here on the Old Homestead all winter."

"I should think it would be lonesome here when so many of the Feathered Friends have gone to the Sunny Southland," said Timid.

"Oh, no," replied Dandy; "for Downy the Woodpecker and Tattler the Jay and Judge Flicker and Redhead the Woodpecker and Whitebreast the Nuthatch and Browny Creeper are all here. And there are Jim Crow and Pesty the Magpie and others. So you see I am not alone."

Timid the Kinglet hid among the Shady Trees where he would not be seen.

"And then I suppose you sometimes see Loxia the Crossbill and others who come down from the Chilly Northland," said Timid.

"Yes, I do. And sometimes Butcher the Shrike comes here, and then I have to watch out for him. He is almost as bad as Sharpshin the Hawk. Of course, I do not see Paddletail the Beaver or Danny Muskrat often after the Glassy Ice covers the Wildwood Pond, but I can visit with Snowshoe the Hare and Jimmy the Swamp Rabbit and Drummer the Grouse. If I want to, I can fly over to the Little Jungle Thicket and see Peter and Molly Cottontail. Out in the Hedgerow by the Apple Orchard is where Bobby White lives; and I sometimes see Ringneck the Pheasant and Hungarian the Partridge. So, you see, I have many neighbors even during Wintry Weather."

Dandy the Chickadee was a fortunate bird. He did not have to go to the Sunny Southland as did the Bluebirds and the Robins and others, and he did not have to fill a Pantry with his Favorite Food as did Trader the Pack Rat.

Trader lived in a Rock Shelter Home in the Black Forest. Every fall he gathered Piñon Nuts and Juicy Bulbs and other Goodies and put them in his Pantry so he would have something to eat on Cold-Cold Days. If Trader could locate some potatoes and such things where he could get them, he would take some of them also.

But, then, Trader had a habit of taking things whether he needed them or not. We would hardly call it stealing, because Trader usually left something else in place of what he took. The worst thing about Trader was that he never made an even trade. He was a cheater. If he saw something he wanted, it would be like him to leave a stone or a stick or a piece of bone in place of it. Whenever Trader the Pack Rat was around, Fearful the Man had to keep his watch and other things where Trader could not find them.

One could tell Trader's home almost as far as he could see it, for there were always piles of trash in his front yard.

Sometimes we see people who are like that. They do not seem to care whether their homes look neat or not. Whenever Trader saw something that he liked, he carried it to his front yard and dropped it. So he always had a pile of stones and sticks and bones and such things on his doorstep.

CHAPTER 8

Growler the Bear Goes to Sleep

GROWLER the Bear had been having a nice time all summer. He really had nothing to do except to hunt for Tempting Berries and Wild Honey and Mushrooms and other Favorite Food. Sometimes he would turn over rocks all day long looking for Ants and Crawly Bugs to eat. And then again he would dig after Dodger the Gopher and Miner the Mole and other little Wild Creatures that suited his taste.

It is a pity that the Wild Creatures kill one another; but that is because there is sin in the world. And the worst killer of all is Terror the Hunter. So, you see, Growler was really not so bad as Terror, who should have known better than to kill God's Wild Creatures.

Sometimes Growler would find a dead cow that a Hot Lightning Flash had killed, or a dead sheep that Sneak the Cougar or Shaggy the Wolf had killed; then he would have a feast. There were some who said that Growler killed them himself, —and sometimes he did; but he was not half so bad as he was painted.

(49)

Growler the Bear had keen ears and a sharp nose.

You see, sometimes Sneak the Cougar would kill a Juicy Calf or something, and after he ate his fill he would leave. Then when he wanted another feast, he would kill something else; for Sneak never cared to eat cold meat. He seldom went back to eat of anything the second time if he could kill another creature. He was a terrible killer, and caught many of Lightfoot the Deer's friends.

After Sneak would leave, along would come Growler the Bear and eat what was left. Of course, whenever people saw his tracks around, they thought that he was the one that had done the killing. So Growler was blamed for many things he did not do.

Growler really was not very bad if he was not bothered. He would run away and hide if anyone came near. He could not see well; and if one kept still, he would not know but that it was a Black Stump he saw. But Growler had keen ears and a sharp nose. Whenever an Enemy came near, the Playful Air Whiffs were always sure to carry Warning Odors to Growler's nose. The Playful Air Whiffs were good friends of Growler's, for they not only told him when Enemies were near but they also led him to his Favorite Food.

One of the things that Growler liked to eat more than anything else was Wild Honey. The honey itself was not wild. Oh, no! We call it Wild Honey because it is made by Wild Bees.

You see, sometimes the home of Buzzer the Bee became too crowded. There were so many Bee Children that the White Box Hive would not hold all of them. Then many of the Bee Children would leave the White Box Hive together and find a new place to live.

If Farmer Smith saw that they were ready to leave, he would give them a new White Box Hive to live in. But sometimes Farmer Smith did not know it, and then they had to find a place for themselves.

When Bees go away by themselves and live in a Hollow Den Tree or in a Jumbled Rock Ledge, we say they are wild. And we call the honey they make, Wild Honey.

There was nothing Growler the Bear liked better than Wild Honey. He could eat gallons of it if he could find it. And he did not seem to mind if Buzzer the Bee stung him.

One day in late fall Growler the Bear was out hunting. He was not hunting for something to eat; that was not it. Growler had eaten much during the Balmy Summer Days and had grown fat and lazy. Of course if he found something to eat that tasted good, he would eat it, but what he was really looking for was a place to sleep.

"Ho-hum, I am getting *so* sleepy," said Growler. "I do wish I could find a nice warm place in which to go to bed."

Then he strolled through the Black Forest, looking first one place and then another for a Cozy Bedroom.

First he tried to crawl into a Warm Hollow Log; but it was so small he could not get inside. Next he found a hole under some rocks; but it was too small also, and not one bit comfortable.

Night after night Growler walked through the Black Forest, looking for a Cozy Bedroom. And night after night was growing colder.

"I believe I will have to dig a Warm Dark

There were so many Bee Children that the
White Box Hive would not hold all of them.

Cave some place," said Growler. But after he had
dug awhile, he came to a Big Rock, and then he
decided he would look around some more.

At last Growler came to a Tired Tree. It was
a large Tired Tree, which the Strong Wind had
blown over.

Growler climbed up on the Tired Tree and
walked along. It must have been lying down a
long time, for there was a row of Dense Bushes
on each side. And at the foot of the Tired Tree
Growler found a regular little Jungle Thicket.

Now it happened that when the Tired Tree had
fallen over, it had torn out a Deep Hole with its
roots. And there it was, partly under the big Tired
Tree and partly covered with Jungle Thicket.

"Aha, this is exactly the place I am looking for," said Growler. "I can make just the kind of Warm Dark Cave I want under this Tired Tree's roots."

And Growler set to work digging out the dirt and stones that were in his way so that he would have a Cozy Bedroom when he was ready to take his all-winter sleep.

CHAPTER 9

Mephitis the Skunk Makes a Bed

"WE simply must find another Hidden Den before Old Man Winter gets here," said Mephitis the Skunk one evening, as he and his family were starting out on their evening stroll.

"Yes, we surely must," said Mrs. Skunk.

Every evening about the time when the Laughing Yellow Sun was winking good night in the Golden West, Mephitis and his family left their Hidden Den and went out in search of Hardshell the Beetle and Jumpy Grasshoppers and other Favorite Food to eat.

Sometimes Mephitis went alone, and Mrs. Skunk went with the Slow Little Skunks. Mephitis was alone the time that Carcajou the Glutton tried to make a meal of him in the Black Forest. Mephitis seldom went to the Black Forest, because he preferred to hunt in the Wide-Wide Pasture and the Green Meadow and the Wood Lot. There were more Crawly Bugs and Jumpy Grasshoppers to be found there.

"Yes, sir; we must look for another Hidden

Den," repeated Mephitis, after all the Slow Little Skunks had come outside.

You see, there were two or three reasons why Mephitis thought he needed to find a new Hidden Den. Mephitis had a large family. It was a large family indeed. There were ten striped backs besides Mrs. Skunk's. It was all right while those ten Young Skunks were little, but now they were almost as large as Mephitis and Mrs. Skunk. You should have seen how crowded that old Hidden Den was! There was scarcely room to turn around when they were all in it. If that Hidden Den had been in any other place, Mephitis could have made it larger. But there it was between some Big Rocks where he could not dig.

Another thing that Mephitis did not like about the old Hidden Den was that it was lousy. Yes, sir; you never saw the like of how many Crawly Lice there were in that Hidden Den. Every time the Skunks came home, those Crawly Lice began to bite them; and many of them even stayed right on them everywhere they went.

Now if that had been a dusty Hidden Den, the Crawly Lice would not have liked it so well. Have you ever seen Old Cluck fluttering in the dust to get the Crawly Lice off her? Of course you have. But Mephitis could not do that because there were so many Big Rocks in his Hidden Den. So he thought it would be a good idea to move away and leave those Crawly Lice.

"Now where shall we go to look for a new Hidden Den?" asked Mrs. Skunk.

"Oh, let's go down into the Green Meadow and catch some Jumpy Grasshoppers," said Skunky Stripe.

"I would rather look for Fat Grubs in the Wood Lot," said Skunky Wunky.

"And I want to look for Tiny the Meadow Mouse down in the Rustling Cornfield," said Skunky Black.

"No, we must find a Hidden Den first," said Mephitis. "It is almost time for Old Man Winter to arrive, and it would never do for us not to be ready when he comes."

Mephitis the Skunk
thought he needed to
find a new Hidden Den.

"Let us go over in the Wide-Wide Pasture," said Mrs. Skunk; "perhaps we can find something to eat there while we are looking for a Hidden Den."

"All right," said Mephitis.

Down through the Tall Grass went Mephitis and Mrs. Skunk, and behind them followed the ten Slow Little Skunks.

Now it happened that as the Skunks reached the Wide-Wide Pasture, Ranger the Coyote was out looking for his breakfast. You see, Ranger never worried about filling a Pantry or fixing a Warm Home for the Wintry Weather. When Old Man Winter came, Ranger slept in Tall Weed Patches or in Tan Strawstacks or in any other place that was the same color that he was, so that he would be well hidden. Then all Ranger had to do was to hunt for something to eat whenever he was hungry.

Ranger saw Skunky Stripe poking along behind the others, and he thought that Skunky Stripe certainly would taste good. But when Ranger made a jump for Skunky Stripe, he saw all the other skunks. Then you should have seen him get away from there.

At last Mrs. Skunk spied a Hidden Den. It was on a High Knoll where the Deep Water would not run into it when the Fleecy Snow melted. Dig-

Ranger the Coyote was out looking for his breakfast.

ger the Badger had made it when he was digging after Dodger the Gopher.

Of course the Hidden Den was too small to hold all of Mephitis's family. So all of them had to get busy and dig it larger. Soon they had a large bedroom dug, and the next thing was to make the bed. But it was not much work to make the bed, for there was plenty of Dry Grass near by. All the Skunks had to do was to rake it with their Long Toenails and drag it inside. Soon they had a nice grassy bed.

Now Mephitis and his family did not sleep all winter as did Johnny Chuck and Tawny Chipmunk and Growler the Bear. And neither did they run around all winter like Snoop the Weasel and Ranger the Coyote and Shadow the Lynx and many others.

When the Cold-Cold Days came, Mephitis and his family crawled into their bedroom and went to sleep; that is, they were quite asleep unless something disturbed them, and then they could awaken. But Tawny Chipmunk and Dodger the Gopher could not wake up even though someone were to dig into their Friendly Burrow, at least not until they were warm.

When Mephitis and his family were ready to go to sleep, they crawled into bed in a circle with their noses all pointing toward the center. But sometimes, when the nights were not too cold, they came out again and ran around for a while. That was the way Worker the Gray Squirrel and Billy Coon did, too.

CHAPTER 10

A Strange Winter Home

NOT far from the Big Jungle Thicket in the Black Forest lived Sticker the Porcupine. At least that was where he lived when he was at home. Perhaps it would be better just to say that he lived in the Black Forest and let it go at that, for Sticker did not seem to know exactly where his home was, and he did not care either.

From the time Sticker was half grown he had wandered through the Wildwoods alone. Evidently he had decided that he was quite able to take care of himself; not that Sticker was a great fighter, or that he could run fast, for he could neither fight nor run. He was entirely too slow to run. He was quite the most dull-witted and sleepy-headed animal in the Black Forest. But what Sticker the Porcupine lacked in speed and fighting ability he made up in another way.

You see, instead of fur, Sticker had many, many Sharp Little Spears covering his back and tail. We call them "quills." So there really was no need for him either to fight or to run.

When an Enemy came near to Sticker, he simply tucked his head under his stomach, bowed his back, and waited, with the Sharp Little Spears sticking out in every direction. Then if Sneak the Cougar or Shadow the Lynx or some other Enemy was so foolish as to try to pounce on him, Sticker swung his tail around and filled the Enemy's face with Sharp Little Spears.

Sticker the Porcupine was not at all sociable. He liked to live alone; that was why he left home when he was half grown. Sometimes Sticker lived in a hole under a rock; but more often he merely climbed into a tree, and there he stayed until he had eaten all the Spicy Bark from it that he wanted. Then he would hunt another tree that suited his taste.

Although Sticker was rather grouchy and liked to live alone, at least he did not bother anyone else. All he asked was that he be let alone. If only he had not killed trees by chewing off their bark he would not have been half bad. But Sticker had to eat something, and chewing the bark off trees was better than killing little Wild Creatures to eat.

Sticker the Porcupine climbed slowly down from the tree where he had been living. That was the only way he could climb, for he always moved slowly. On the ground he walked with short, slow

Sticker the Porcupine was not at all sociable.

steps as if he had all the time he wanted and no place in particular to go.

Far back in the Wildwood, Sticker came to an old cabin. Someone had been camping there not long before. Sticker thought he would look around and see if he could find some salt. If there was one thing that Sticker liked more than another, it was salt. He would eat an entire board if it were covered with a little salty grease.

The first thing Sticker found was an old leather glove. Someone had perspired while wearing it, and it tasted salty. Sticker ate it with relish, and then went around back of the cabin. There he found where the cook had emptied out a dish of beans that he had salted too much, and Sticker cleaned them up.

By that time he was feeling quite satisfied. He decided it was time to get ready for Old Man Winter. Overhead there were many Gray Cloud Ships sailing across the sky, and it looked much as if the Fleecy Snow would come dancing down before very long.

Now where do you suppose Sticker spends the Wintry Weather? Why, high up in a tree where he sits in the freezing breath of Old Man Winter. Can you imagine anyone's choosing such an uncomfortable place as that?

But that suited Sticker, so he started out to find a tree that was exactly the kind he liked.

At last he found one he thought would do. It was a Young Pine Tree, and Sticker thought the bark would be good.

Fisher the Bold was a fierce fighter.

As Sticker was ready to climb slowly up the tree, he heard a noise. He did not wait to see who made it, but raised his back and tucked his nose under his stomach.

Sticker did it barely in time, too, for no sooner had he ruffed up his Sharp Little Spears than Fisher the Bold grabbed him by the throat. Sticker swung his tail and struck a strong blow against his Enemy. Twice he drove in the Sharp Little Spears before Fisher the Bold would let go of Sticker the Porcupine's throat.

Fisher the Bold was a fierce fighter. He showed his White Fangs and hissed. He would not think anything of killing and eating his cousin Killer the Marten if he had a chance.

But Fisher the Bold decided he had had enough for one day. He had taken the slow-moving Sticker for an easy mark, but it did not take long for him to see that he had been mistaken.

So while Fisher the Bold limped painfully on his way, Sticker the Porcupine climbed his tree, where he would stay during the Cold-Cold Days, or at least he would stay there until he needed more Spicy Bark to eat.

No doubt the next time Fisher the Bold met Sticker, he gave him plenty of room; he had had one lesson he would not forget right away.

Perhaps one reason why Sticker chose to stay in a tree and let Old Man Winter blow his icy breath on him was that he felt safer from his Enemies. But that was surely a queer place to live.

CHAPTER 11

The First Snow

DID you ever awaken some morning in the fall and see the Merry Little Snowflakes coming softly down for the first time that year? Of course you have, and that is what Bud and Mary Smith did on the Old Homestead.

For two days the Gray Cloud Ships had been sailing over with their loads of Fleecy Snow, and at last they had decided to empty some out. There it was sifting down as quietly as anything when Bud and Mary looked out one morning. Already the Soft White Blanket was up to their shoe tops.

"Oh, what fun we shall have at school today!" exclaimed Mary, when they were ready to start. "We can play Fox and Geese and make Snow Angels and build Snow Men and everything."

"Yes, and when we get home we can go coasting on the Long Hill," said Bud.

"Let us play Follow the Leader on the way to school this morning," suggested Mary. "You go first, and I will follow."

Away they went down the road toward school, with Bud breaking a path.

Virginia Opossum went into her Warm Hollow
Log and curled up for a nap.

But Bud and Mary and the other children were
not the only ones who were having a fine time in
the Fleecy Snow. No, sir. There were Junco the
Snowbird and Snowy the Bunting. It was the
kind of day they both liked, and they were having
heaps of fun flying across the field with their
friends and alighting on the Fleecy Snow. What
a good time they had!

You see, both Junco the Snowbird and Snowy
the Bunting like company, and they always have
ten or twenty friends with them. Perhaps you will
wonder where they could find anything to eat
when the Fleecy Snow was so deep; but it was no
trick at all for them. They could always find Tall
Weed Stalks sticking up through the Fleecy Snow

on which they could alight and make a good meal of the Tiny Seeds.

Junco the Snowbird lived on the Old Homestead part of the time, but sometimes he went for a visit farther south if the Wintry Weather became too cold. But Snowy the Bunting was entirely different; he never saw the Old Homestead except in Wintry Weather, and some years he did not visit it at all. Snowy the Bunting's real home was in the Far-Far North in the Land of Ice, where Arctic the White Fox and Ovibos the Musk Ox lived. That was where Snowy the Bunting lived much of the time. But sometimes, while many of the Feathered Friends from the Old Homestead were playing in the Sunny Southland, Snowy would come down to the Old Homestead for a visit. He liked a change, you know.

It must have seemed to Snowy almost like going to the Sunny Southland to visit the Old Homestead after living in the Land of Ice. So Snowy the Bunting always had a fine time.

"We must be going to have a hard winter," said Mr. Smith to Mrs. Smith; "because Snowy the Bunting is with us already."

No doubt that is what the Furry Friends thought. My, but how they did hurry around when the Merry Little Snowflakes began to fall!

Growler the Bear had finished his Warm Dark Cave under the roots of the Tired Tree and was in the Big Jungle Thicket looking for some Dried Berries to eat when the Fleecy Snow started to fall in the night.

"I believe I will go home and go to bed," he said to himself.

Away went Growler through the Blackberry Brambles and Twining Vines toward his Warm Dark Cave. Soon he was curled up as comfortable as anything. For a while Growler could not seem to go to sleep. He was restless and took only little naps, and he growled as if he were having a bad dream. But after a few days, if you had looked into Growler's Warm Dark Cave, you would have seen him sound asleep. The Merry Little Snowflakes covered Growler's doorway with a Soft White Blanket, and there he slept until Jolly Spring came back and awakened him.

Growler the Bear was not the only one who had gone to bed when the Merry Little Snowflakes came dancing down. Tawny Chipmunk and Johnny Chuck were already snoring in their Snug Beds, and so was Dodger the Gopher. Billy Coon was looking for something to eat down along Little River. He didn't find much, so he went home to his Hollow Den Tree, which stood near the bridge that crossed Little River. He thought he would sleep at least awhile, until the storm was over.

Digger the Badger had made a Deep Burrow, and in it he went to sleep as Growler the Bear had done. Digger's legs were short, and he did not like to plod through deep Fleecy White Snow, because his stomach had to drag in it.

Virginia Opossum went into her Warm Hollow Log in the Wood Lot and curled up for a nap. And, of course, Mephitis and his large family were sound asleep with their noses almost touching in the middle of their new Hidden Den. Even Forktongue the Snake and the Wriggly Earthworms had crawled deep into the Soft Warm Earth and gone to sleep.

There surely were a lot of sleepyheads on the Old Homestead, but there were also many Wild Creatures that were wide-awake. Downy the Woodpecker and his cousin Redhead were as busy as usual looking for Tree Borers, and so was their large cousin Judge Flicker. Dandy the Chickadee and his cousin Whitebreast the Nuthatch were running a race to see who could find the greater number of Tree Grubs; and Timid the Kinglet flitted about, saying: "I told you Old Man Winter was coming."

Then there was Shadow the Lynx, who was trying to catch Snowshoe the Hare in the Fleecy Snow; and there were Molly and Peter Cottontail, who were hopping around in the shelter of their Little Jungle Thicket. Pesty the Magpie and his undesirable cousins Tattler the Jay and Jim Crow were out looking to see what mischief they could find to get into. Wasn't it strange how Old Man Winter could put some of the Wild Creatures to sleep and make others work harder than ever?

CHAPTER 12

The Trail of Snoop the Weasel

YOU will remember that when the Wintry Weather came, Snowshoe the Hare put on a white coat. That is exactly what Snoop the Weasel did also. During the Balmy Summer Days Snoop wore a brown coat; but when the Cold-Cold Days came, he changed it for white.

You see, if Snoop wore a brown coat during Wintry Weather, everyone could see him when he ran about on the Fleecy Snow. His enemies would see him and catch him. And if Snoop were hunting in a brown coat, everyone would see him coming and run away.

Snoop had been wearing his new white coat only a little while when the first Fleecy Snow came. His brown one had gradually dropped off, and the white one had grown in its place.

So Snoop was glad to see the Fleecy Snow, for then his coat matched it. Before the Fleecy Snow came, he had been running around among the Dead Grass and Brown Leaflets in his white coat, and that was almost as bad as running around in a brown coat on the Fleecy Snow.

"I believe I will go hunting," said Snoop the Weasel, when he came out of his Friendly Burrow and saw all that Fleecy Snow falling.

Snoop hunted in the daytime as well as at night, although he really would rather hunt at night. This time when Snoop made up his mind to go hunting it was morning. Snoop thought that if he went hunting in the morning, he would find more of the Little Wild Creatures at home, and then he could pounce upon them. He also thought that Great Horn the Owl and some of his own Enemies would be hiding and would not catch him. So Snoop started out in the Fleecy Snow.

First he went to the Rustling Cornfield. He thought he might be lucky enough to find Tiny the Meadow Mouse eating the Tempting Kernels away from the shelter of a Friendly Burrow.

"Sniff, sniff," went Snoop the Weasel; "I smell Tiny hiding in this Rustling Corn Shock."

Now it happened that Tiny was sitting just out of sight eating Tempting Kernels when Snoop stopped by that Rustling Corn Shock.

"I must run and hide," thought Tiny, and away he ran to his Soft Little Bed in his Friendly Burrow under the Rustling Corn Shock. So when Snoop slipped into the Rustling Corn Shock, Tiny was nowhere to be seen.

Snoop the Weasel was glad to see the Fleecy
Snow, for his coat matched it.

"Sniff, sniff," went Snoop, and soon he had
found Tiny's Friendly Burrow. "I don't believe
Tiny is worth digging after," said he, and he went
to look for something else.

Snoop really was not much of a digger, anyway, for his little feet were covered with hair, and
his toenails were not large enough to dig well.

From the Rustling Cornfield Snoop went to the
Wood Lot. He thought he might find Hungarian
the Partridge hiding under one of the Stubby Little
Bushes. But Hungarian the Partridge was over in
the Fence Row picking the Tempting Kernels
from Wild Sunflowers.

"Now I wonder where I should go next,"
thought Snoop. "I believe I will visit the Hedge-

row, and perhaps I can catch one of Bobby White's family."

Over by the Hedgerow Bobby White and his family were wondering where they could find something to eat themselves.

"Let us fly over to the Rustling Cornfield and pick some Tempting Kernels from the Rustling Corn Shocks," said Bobby.

You see, the Soft White Blanket had covered almost everything that Bobby could eat at the Hedgerow. So away they flew to the Rustling Cornfield just before Snoop the Weasel came to the Hedgerow.

"Well, well, I see that Bobby and his family have gone," said Snoop, for he could see Scratchy Little Tracks in the Fleecy Snow where Bobby had been. "Now I wonder if Molly Cottontail is in her Friendly Burrow in the Little Jungle Thicket. I'll go over there and catch her before she can get out of her Friendly Burrow."

Down along the Hedgerow went Snoop the Weasel, sniffing into every hole and under every Stubby Little Bush that he passed. Snoop wanted to go over to Farmer Smith's Chicken House, but he was afraid that Nero the Hound might see him. How good those chickens smelled! And there was the Granary, where Whiskers the Mouse and his friends liked to play when Spot the Skunk left them alone.

Spot the Skunk was a small cousin of Mephitis the Skunk, and he lived under the Granary most of the time. In fact, he was asleep under the Granary right then; but Snoop did not know it.

"I do hope that Molly is at home," said Snoop the Weasel.

When Snoop arrived at the Little Jungle Thicket, there was Nero digging in Molly's Friendly Burrow as hard as he could. It was not a very nice thing for Nero the Hound to do, but all of us do things that are not very nice sometimes. Of course, Nero could never dig deep enough to catch Molly, for he would have to make too large

There was Nero digging in Molly's Friendly Burrow.

a hole before he could crawl in. But Nero liked to dig, anyway. Perhaps that was his way of getting warm.

"I'll run right along to my own Friendly Burrow before Nero sees me," said Snoop the Weasel to himself. And away he hopped, leaving a Crooked Little Trail in the Fleecy Snow.

Chapter 13

Reddy Fox Plays a Joke

"THIS is the day I have been waiting for," said Trapper Jim, as he looked out of his cabin window and saw the Merry Little Snowflakes dancing down. "I'll take some traps and go out and set them."

You see, Trapper Jim thought he could track the Furbearers while there was Fleecy Snow on the ground, and then he could find their Hidden Dens. Later he could set traps there and catch them.

After Trapper Jim had eaten his breakfast, he put on his warmest cap and coat and mittens and started out with a bunch of traps over his shoulder. Across the Broad Fields he tramped, looking here and there for Crooked Little Trails that the Furbearers had made.

Trapper Jim saw many, many tracks that Jack the Jumper and his friends had made. And once he saw where Ranger the Coyote had been chasing Jack through the Fleecy Snow.

Ranger liked to hunt Jack the Jumper while the Fleecy Snow was soft and deep, because then

Jack could not run so fast. But Ranger could run swiftly through the deep Fleecy Snow because his legs were longer and stronger.

"Ranger was certainly making Jack run," said Trapper Jim, when he saw their tracks in the Fleecy Snow; "see how far Jack jumped each time."

After a while Trapper Jim saw a Crooked Little Trail. "It looks as if Snoop the Weasel has been along here," he said. "I believe that I will follow his Crooked Little Trail and see if I can find his Friendly Burrow. He must be wearing his winter coat now."

Trapper Jim never set his traps except in Wintry Weather, because that was the only time when fur was good. When the Cold-Cold Days came, the Furbearers put on heavy coats so they would be warm. That was the time when Trapper Jim said there fur was "prime." Trapper Jim knew that he could not sell Snoop's fur unless it was white, because it was not prime when it was brown. That was what he meant when he said Snoop must be wearing his winter coat.

Trapper Jim followed Snoop's Crooked Little Trail through the Fleecy Snow. Sometimes he saw where Snoop had dived under the Fleecy Snow out of sight and walked along for a way.

Trapper Jim saw many, many tracks that Jack
the Jumper and his friends had made.

Perhaps that was when Snoop was hiding from
an Enemy; or he may have been sniffing along to
see if he could smell Barney the Shrew. Barney
liked to make Secret Little Tunnels under the
Fleecy Snow so he could run around without being seen.

At last Trapper Jim came to the end of Snoop's
Crooked Little Trail, and there it went down into
his Friendly Burrow.

"I have found where Snoop is living, and now
I will set a trap for him," said Trapper Jim. "Tomorrow I will surely have him when I come back."

So Trapper Jim set a trap right in front of
Snoop's Friendly Burrow, where he would be sure
to step into it when he came out, and covered it

(81)

6—W. C.

with some Fleecy Snow. Then he put a piece of Tempting Bait on the end of a stick and stuck it up by the trap. He thought Snoop would jump up after the Tempting Bait and would come down into the trap. Then Trapper Jim went on looking for more Crooked Little Trails to follow.

Now it happened that there was another one looking for Crooked Little Trails, and that was Reddy Fox. Reddy was trying to find Bunny Tracks leading to a Cozy Form. He thought that he could sneak up in the Fleecy Snow and pounce upon a Sleeping Bunny.

Reddy had been over in the Black Forest looking for Drummer the Grouse; but when he did find Drummer, he was sitting on a High Limb where Reddy could not catch him. Reddy Fox could not climb trees that were standing up straight, but his cousin Mr. Gray Fox could.

That was the way it was with the bears. Growler the Black Bear could climb trees, but his fierce cousin Growler the Grizzly Bear could not.

Reddy Fox had decided to leave the Black Forest and look for the Crooked Little Trails of Bunnies.

Suddenly, while Reddy was walking along, he came to Trapper Jim's tracks. "Aha, I see that Trapper Jim is out with his traps again," said

Reddy Fox, "for he is following Snoop the Weasel's Crooked Little Trail. I'll follow Trapper Jim's trail and see if I can steal some Tempting Bait."

You see, Reddy Fox knew that every winter Trapper Jim set traps for the Furbearers. He had set traps many times for Reddy Fox himself, but Reddy had been too smart to walk into them. He had a keen nose, and the Playful Air Whiffs always told him where Trapper Jim's traps were.

Reddy Fox knew that Trapper Jim usually put some Tempting Bait on a stick when he set a trap, for Reddy had followed his tracks many times. He had stolen the Tempting Bait many times, and that was what he planned to do again.

Reddy knew that chicken heads don't grow on sticks.

Sure enough, after Reddy had followed Trapper Jim's tracks a way, he saw a Tempting Bait where Jim had set a trap for Snoop the Weasel. The Tempting Bait was a chicken's head.

"Now I wonder if Trapper Jim thinks that anyone is so stupid as to believe that a chicken's head grows on a stick," said Reddy Fox. "That is like putting up a sign that says: 'Here is a trap; be careful.'"

Reddy Fox sniffed around in the Fleecy Snow until he found where Trapper Jim had set his trap. "I believe I will play a joke on Trapper Jim," said Reddy.

Very carefully he dragged the trap out of the Fleecy Snow and turned it upside down. "My, but won't Trapper Jim be angry when he sees that!" said Reddy. Then he grabbed the chicken head and ran away.

That was once when Reddy Fox did a friendly turn for Snoop the Weasel.

CHAPTER 14

Bud Smith Plays Santa Claus

"I WONDER if the Feathered Friends aren't getting hungry," said Bud Smith one day after school. "I don't see where they can find anything to eat."

It was almost two weeks after the first Fleecy Snow had fallen, and the ground was still covered with a Soft White Blanket.

"Let's take some food to them," suggested Mary.

"But we have no place to put it," said Bud. "They can't find it if we throw it in the Fleecy Snow."

"That is right," said Mary, "but maybe we could clean away the Fleecy Snow first."

"I know what we can do," said Bud; "let's build a regular Feeding Place."

"Oh, won't that be fine!" said Mary. "Then we can watch the Feathered Friends when they are at lunch sometimes."

"You run and get the snow shovel, and I will get the other things together," said Bud, and away he ran toward the Workshop.

In a little while Bud and Mary were all ready

"It looks as if Bobby White will have lots of company at his Feeding Place," said Mary.

to start. Bud had a hammer and a saw and a can of nails, and he had picked out an armful of boards and sticks from the pile in the Workshop.

"Where shall we build it?" asked Mary.

"Let's build it in the Apple Orchard by the Hedgerow," said Bud. "The Hedgerow and the Apple Trees will help to protect it, and it will be near enough for us to go there often with Favorite Food for the Feathered Friends, but not so close as to frighten them away."

"I think that is a fine place," agreed Mary, "and it will be handy for Bobby White and his family, who make their home in the Hedgerow."

First, Bud shoveled the Fleecy Snow away from the spot where the Feeding Place was to be built, and then he and Mary carried the tools and boards there and laid them on the ground.

"I believe I will make Bobby White's Feeding Place first," said Bud. "We will use these four sticks for corners, and brace them up with these strips. Then we will lay a few poles across the top, and after that I will carry out some armfuls of Seedy Millet and cover it over. That will keep the Fleecy Snow from falling on the ground again, and we can throw Bobby's feed under there. I know he will feel safer while he is eating if he has something over him to hide him from Flying Enemies. And the Feathered Friends can eat the Seedy Millet."

By the time Bobby White's Feeding Place was finished, it was too dark to do any more work that day, so Bud and Mary scattered some of Old Cluck's Mixed Grains and an armful of Seedy Millet under the shelter, and left.

That evening, on the Kitchen Table, Bud made a box. It was covered over the top, but one end was open. Sticking out from the front side at the bottom were two thin, wide boards like the tail of a windmill. In the bottom of the box was a small bolt on which the box could turn. When the Playful Air Whiffs blew against the thin, wide boards, they would turn the box around with the open end away so they would not blow Fleecy Snow into it.

When Bud and Mary came home from school the next afternoon, they hurried out to the Feeding Place to fasten up the box.

"Oh, see there!" exclaimed Mary, when they were in sight of the Feeding Place. "That looks like Ringneck the Pheasant."

"So it is," said Bud; "and there is Hungarian the Partridge also."

"It looks as if Bobby White will have lots of company at his Feeding Place," said Mary.

In a little while Bud had the box fastened on a stick that was nailed to one corner of the Feeding Place. "Now what shall we put into it?" Mary asked.

"Well, let's see," said Bud. "We can crush some dry bread for one thing; and we can grind some Tempting Nut Meats and mix with it. Then I can put in some Seedy Millet, and I can find plenty of Weed Seeds in the Granary where Father cleaned his seed grain."

"Tap-tap-tap-tap," went someone on an Apple Tree; "tap-tap-tap-tap."

"Oh, there is Redhead the Woodpecker! and we haven't given him anything to eat yet. He is trying to tell us he is here."

"We must get a chunk of suet and nail it to a

tree for Redhead and Downy and Judge Flicker and Whitebreast the Nuthatch and the others that do not eat seeds," said Bud. "I'll ask Father to get some the first time he is in town. Of course it is easier for those Feathered Friends to find something to eat than it is for the ones that eat seeds and grains, for the Tree Grubs are not covered with Fleecy Snow."

That evening Mrs. Smith helped Bud and Mary fix a Breakfast Nook for Redhead the Woodpecker and his friends. First she chopped up some meat scraps very fine. Then she melted some tallow and put the meat scraps into it.

"Now run to the Woodshed and bring a large piece of Rough Bark," said Mrs. Smith.

"Tap-tap-tap-tap," went someone on an Apple Tree. It was Redhead the Woodpecker!

When Bud returned with the Rough Bark, Mrs. Smith poured the melted tallow and meat scraps into the deep cracks. Soon the tallow was hard again, and then all Bud had to do was to fasten the piece of Rough Bark where the Woodpeckers would see it.

"I hope Redhead and his friends like their Breakfast Nook," said Mrs. Smith.

The next day Bud nailed the Breakfast Nook to a tree near the Feeding Place.

"I think we should give the Feathered Friends some warm water each morning," he said.

So Bud placed a crock in a box of oats so the water would not freeze so quickly, and set it on the ground in front of the Feeding Place, where Bobby White could use it as well as the others.

"I believe I will tie some bundles of Seedy Millet and Cane Tops along on the Hedgerow for good measure," said Bud; "and then there will be room for all the Feathered Friends."

CHAPTER 15

A Neighborhood Fight

NOISY the English Sparrow was the worst nuisance on the Old Homestead. He was not satisfied to fuss and chatter and scold with other Sparrows, but he was always worrying and bullying the other Feathered Friends. Although Noisy had a perfectly good Nesting Place on a beam under the roof of the Rambling Old Barn in summer, he was never contented to stay at home and mind his own business. He was a regular busybody.

He spent so much time meddling in the affairs of other Feathered Friends that frequently his own babies cried because they were hungry. He actually neglected to feed them sometimes when he was interested in picking a fuss with his neighbors. He made a nuisance of himself.

Of course Noisy the English Sparrow was not wholly to blame. You see, years ago some of his family were brought to America from England. People thought he would work as any good citizen should to rid the country of Troublesome Insects. But instead of doing that he became a pest. He

Cardinal the Grosbeak wore a scarlet coat.

found so many other things to eat that he paid little attention to eating insects.

Even though Noisy was not to blame for being in America, it does seem as if he could have lived like a gentleman; but, instead, he preferred to make life miserable for everyone around him, and he disgraced the whole Sparrow family.

When Noisy had nothing else to do, he would call all his friends together, and they would start out on a flight around the Old Homestead. They would stop here and there long enough to fuss with anyone that might live wherever they stopped. In the Balmy Summer Days they would flock to the Big Elm in the front yard by the Grand Old House and annoy Weaver the Oriole, who had his nest there. Then they would fly down to

(92)

Butcher the Shrike lived in the Far Northland
and visited the Old Homestead only during the Wintry Weather.

the Red Cedar and scold Robin Red and the Blue-birds. From there they would go to the eaves of the Grand Old House to see what Jenny Wren was doing. Jenny Wren could scold about as loudly as the Sparrows, and, what is more, if they became too fierce, she could enter her home through the knothole under the eaves, and leave them to fuss among themselves. Jenny's home was one place that Noisy the English Sparrow had never been able to enter.

One Cold-Cold Day in winter Noisy and his friends were holding a meeting on the hayrack that was standing near the Rambling Old Barn. As usual they were trying their best to see which could make the most noise. They were all chattering at once. Noisy was not at all polite, for he never kept still when others were speaking. Instead of waiting, he chattered the louder.

Suddenly a bluish-gray bird about the size of Robin Red dived into their midst; and before they could collect their scattered wits, he had killed one of Noisy's friends. It was Butcher the Shrike who had paid them a visit.

Butcher the Shrike lived in the Far Northland. He never visited the Old Homestead except during Wintry Weather when he could not find food in his frozen country.

Butcher the Shrike had a very cruel habit. Sometimes when he caught more mice and other things than he could eat, he would find a sharp thorn or a barbed fence, and there he would hang them until he was hungry again. Butcher really preferred mice; but he liked sparrow, too.

Butcher the Shrike was a queer bird. He had a powerful head and a hooked beak like Dart the Sparrow Hawk's; but he did not wear long, curved, needlelike claws like Dart's. His feet were more like Robin Red's or any other bird's that sits on a perch.

When Butcher the Shrike dropped down in the midst of Noisy and his friends, away they flew to find some other place where they could fuss. It happened that they went to the Apple Orchard, and, of course, the first thing they saw was the Feeding Place that Bud and Mary had built for their Feathered Friends.

"Oh, let's take possession of the Feeding Place," said Noisy, and soon they were sitting all around on it, chattering and scolding and making a big noise.

In a little while Tattler the Jay came along and added his coarse voice to the noise. Some of the other Feathered Friends refused to leave merely because Noisy and his friends came, and in no time there was a neighborhood fight going on.

"Listen to that noise out in the Apple Orchard," said Hunting Cat to himself; "I believe I will see what is the matter. Perhaps, while the Feathered Friends are fighting among themselves, I can pounce upon one."

Noisy should have had more sense than to make such a racket. He should have known that it would tell all the Enemies where the Feeding Place was.

So there was Hunting Cat sneaking out along the Hedgerow, while Noisy and his friends fussed with the other Feathered Friends to see who would have the Feeding Place. It was a wonder that Noisy could not have eaten peaceably as the other Feathered Friends did. Bobby White was quite disgusted, and he and his family left.

Now almost the first Feathered Friend that Hunting Cat saw was Cardinal the Grosbeak. Of course, he would see him first, because he was so conspicuous in his scarlet coat on the Fleecy Snow. Hunting Cat sneaked along the Hedgerow, and all the while there was that neighborhood fight going on.

"I'm quite sure I can catch Cardinal the Grosbeak while he is sitting on the ground," said Hunting Cat to himself. "Yes, sir; I'm sure I can."

It was a good thing for Hunting Cat that Bud Smith did not see him sneaking over to the Feeding Place to catch Feathered Friends.

CHAPTER 16

Hunting Cat Makes a Raid

HUNTING CAT was like almost everyone else; he was nice in some ways, but in other ways he was bad. He helped to keep Whiskers the Mouse and his many friends from destroying Farmer Smith's grain and from chewing holes in things that they should not. And Hunting Cat helped to keep Mr. Barn Rat from stealing Old Cluck's Chicklets and eggs. But there was one thing about Hunting Cat that no one liked—that was his habit of catching the Feathered Friends.

Of course Hunting Cat was no worse than Terror the Hunter when it came to killing Feathered Friends. Terror would take his Flashing Gun and tramp across the Broad Fields and over the Green Meadows and along Singing Rivers and by Quiet Lakes in search of Feathered Friends and Furry Friends. He would have killed almost everything, even down to the last one, if Friendly Folk had not made laws to stop him.

So Hunting Cat really was no worse than Terror the Hunter, because Terror should have known better. Bud Smith had tried to teach Hunt-

(97)

ing Cat not to kill the Feathered Friends. But Hunting Cat was like all other cats, he would not be taught anything. He always had plenty of good food to eat, but still he would hunt Feathered Friends.

One time during the Balmy Summer Days Bud had seen Hunting Cat sneaking on Burlingame the Lark. No doubt Hunting Cat would have caught Burlingame if Bud had not thrown a rock and frightened him away, for, for some reason or other, Burlingame liked to spend most of his time on the ground. That was where Hunting Cat could catch him.

Then Bud thought of a scheme to protect the Feathered Friends against Hunting Cat. He bought a Tinkly Little Bell and put it on a collar, and made Hunting Cat wear it on his neck. Every

Blue Darter was a fierce murderer; and whenever he visited the Old Homestead, all the Little Wild Creatures quaked with fear.

time Hunting Cat would try to sneak on a Feathered Friend the Tinkly Little Bell would say: "Tinkle, tinkle, tinkle; here comes Hunting Cat. Beware, beware!"

Then the Feathered Friends would fly away. But when Hunting Cat was sitting quietly waiting for Mr. Barn Rat to come out of his Dark Hole, the Tinkly Little Bell was quiet also, and did not give a warning. So it did not stop Hunting Cat from doing good, but it helped to stop him from doing harm.

When the Wintry Weather came and Hunting Cat stayed around the Grand Old House and the Rambling Old Barn most of the time, Bud decided that he did not need to wear his Tinkly Little Bell. So Bud had taken it off until Jolly Spring brought the Feathered Friends back from the Sunny Southland again. That was why Hunting Cat was not wearing his Tinkly Little Bell when he started for the Feeding Place by the Hedgerow.

Slowly Hunting Cat sneaked along the Hedgerow toward the Feeding Place. The Hedgerow made the best kind of hiding place for him. In a little while he was near enough so that he could almost spring on Cardinal the Grosbeak. A few more steps and he would be near enough. Hunting Cat had not the least idea that anyone saw him.

Now it happened that there was on the Old Homestead just then a visitor who seldom came there. His home was in the Chilly Northland, and he only came to the Old Homestead in the middle of the Wintry Weather, when his Favorite Food was scarce in his own land. His name was Blue Darter the Goshawk.

Blue Darter was a fierce murderer; and whenever he visited the Old Homestead in the dead of winter, all the Little Wild Creatures quaked with fear. Why, Blue Darter would as soon go right into the Chicken House and kill Old Cluck as not, if he had a chance; and he didn't care if Mr. Smith was watching, either.

But Blue Darter was especially fond of grouse and rabbit and ptarmigan.

Whitetail the Ptarmigan belonged to the same family as Drummer the Grouse, and he lived among the High Mountain Peaks. During the Balmy Summer Days he wore a brown and black and white coat; but when Old Man Winter came, he put on a white coat as Snoop the Weasel and Snowshoe the Hare did. Then it was harder for Blue Darter the Goshawk to see him when he was sitting on the Fleecy Snow.

Sometimes when Blue Darter grew tired of looking for Whitetail the Ptarmigan, he would

come to the Old Homestead in search of Snowshoe the Hare and Molly Cottontail and Drummer the Grouse. That was what he was doing
when he saw Hunting Cat sneaking along the
Hedgerow after Cardinal the Grosbeak.

Now it may have been that Blue Darter
thought Hunting Cat was Molly or Peter Cottontail. And then again he may have known it was
not. He may have been very hungry. But whatever it was that caused him to do it, it was unusual
for him to think of catching Hunting Cat. Blue
Darter generally didn't bother him.

There was Hunting Cat sitting in the Hedgerow all ready to pounce upon Cardinal the Grosbeak, when down swooped Blue Darter and
grabbed for him. It was a wonder that Blue Darter
did not carry Hunting Cat away, for it was seldom
indeed that he ever missed his prey. But Hunting
Cat was very quick. He was much quicker than
Molly would have been. Molly would probably
have merely sat there and let Blue Darter grab
her, because she would have been so frightened.
If that was what Blue Darter expected Hunting
Cat to do, he was mistaken.

Into the Hedgerow jumped Hunting Cat so
quickly that all Blue Darter did was to tear a big
gash in Hunting Cat's coat with his sharp claws.

"Now how do you suppose Hunting Cat got hurt?" said Bud that night, when he noticed the big gash. But Hunting Cat never would have told even if he could have talked, for he knew he should not have been trying to catch the Feathered Friends. That was a fair warning for him to stay away from the Feeding Place.

CHAPTER 17

Shaggy the Wolf Is Hungry

"YOW-OOOOOO," howled Shaggy the Wolf one crisp, wintry evening; "I am very hungry."

"Yow-oooooo," answered a friend from over in a Blue Spruce Thicket; "I am hungry, too."

"Let's go hunting," howled Shaggy. "We will go out on the Broad Prairie and chase Jack the Jumper."

Shaggy had been hidden all day in a Wild Plum Thicket in the Black Forest. He was cold and hungry, and he wanted to run around awhile and get warm. For many days the Fleecy Snow had covered the ground, and Shaggy had had a hard time to find anything to eat.

"Yow-oooooo," he howled; "hurry up; I am almost starved."

In a little while Shaggy's friend sneaked out of his Blue Spruce Thicket and came loping across the Fleecy Snow to the place where Shaggy was waiting. Overhead the Smiling Moon was shining brightly, and the Black Tree Tops were mak-

"Yow-ooooo," howled Shaggy the Wolf one crisp
wintry evening; "I am very hungry."

ing Long Shadows on the Fleecy Snow. It was
the kind of night that Prowler liked.

"Hoe-hoe-hoe," said Great Horn the Owl, as
he awoke after sleeping all day; "I hear Shaggy
the Wolf and his friend. They must be going
hunting."

Over on his Rocky Ledge Sneak the Cougar
screamed fiercely, and in the Willow Thicket by
Paddletail the Beaver's Wildwood Pond, Shadow
the Lynx sneaked noiselessly along searching for
Snowshoe the Hare. Paddletail the Beaver and
Danny Muskrat were both feasting safely on their
Favorite Foods under the Glassy Ice. And
Growler the Bear had been sound asleep in his
Warm Dark Cave for many, many days. A Win-

try Night was a weird time in the Black Forest.

Down through the Wildwood Lanes ran Shaggy the Wolf and his friend. Shaggy usually liked to have company when he went hunting, for then it was easier for him to catch something. Many times while his friend was running along behind, he had cut across and caught their prey. They had hunted together many times, and each one knew his part well. Two often had better success.

Out on the Broad Prairie, Jack the Jumper was nibbling Fragrant Sagebrush in the Bright Moonlight. Only the night before he had had a race with Ranger the Coyote. And several times he had seen Reddy Fox sneaking along through the Rabbit Bushes. So Jack the Jumper was watching. He did not dare to be off guard for an instant.

Then Jack thought he saw a Shadowy Form running along over the Broad Prairie. Sure enough, in a moment it came closer, and right behind it was another.

"That must be Shaggy the Wolf and his friend, for he is larger than Ranger the Coyote," said Jack the Jumper. "They must be following my Crooked Little Trail. I believe it is time for me to run away from here before they see me."

But Jack the Jumper had not started soon

enough. Almost as soon as he had made his first long jump Shaggy's sharp eyes had seen him.

"Yow-oooooo, there goes Jack the Jumper," he howled to Prowler. And then you should have seen how fast they ran after poor Jack. And how they did howl! It was enough to make Jack's heart stop beating.

Whatever else Shaggy the Wolf may have been, he was no fool. He knew that in a fair race it would be doubtful if he could catch Jack. But Shaggy thought he could run faster in the Fleecy Snow than Jack could; at least he thought he saw a chance to cut across turns and catch Jack while his friend was chasing him.

Sometimes Shaggy had another trick that he

Jack the Jumper was nibbling
Fragrant Sagebrush.

used when he was hunting with his friend. He knew that Jack the Jumper and his friends did not do much turning when they ran unless something was in their way. They would simply start out across the Broad Prairie, and how they would fly! They leaped through the air.

So instead of both Shaggy and his friend running after them, they would sometimes take turns at it. First, one would run awhile, and then, while he was resting, the other one would run. In that way they could tire out Jack's friends and catch them. That was what they planned to do with Jack if they could not get him cornered in the Deep Fleecy Snow.

But Jack the Jumper had some clever tricks of his own that Shaggy the Wolf was to learn before the night was over.

Out on the Broad Prairie the Playful Air Whiffs played many tricks. One of them was to look for the Bare Ridges and then blow all the Fleecy Snow off. Yes, sir; they would pick up the Fleecy Snow from the Bare Ridges and carry it to the Low Gullies. There they would make it into Deep Snowdrifts.

Now Jack the Jumper always went to the Bare Ridges to find something to eat where the Fleecy Snow did not cover his Favorite Food. And then, you see, he knew that if an Enemy came, he could run very fast where there was no Fleecy Snow. That was where Jack was sitting when Shaggy and his friend spied him.

Along that Bare Ridge raced Jack almost as if he had wings. And right behind him came Shaggy and his friend as fast as they could, with their Red Tongues hanging out and their White Fangs showing. In anticipation they tasted the feast they were sure they would have before long.

At last Jack the Jumper was almost to the end of the Bare Ridge. "Yow-oooooo," howled Shaggy, "let's hurry, and we will catch Jack now. We are almost upon him."

But Jack the Jumper had another trick that he had not yet played on Shaggy and his friend. Right where the Bare Ridge ended was where a Low Gully started. And in the Low Gully was a Deep Snowdrift. On the top of the Deep Snow-drift was a Hard Little Crust. Jack knew it was strong enough to hold him, for he had run across it many times. So he jumped out on it and skimmed along as fast as if it were a race track.

But, oh, dear, you should have seen Shaggy and his friend when they tried to run along on the Hard Little Crust! Into the Deep Snowdrift they went clear up to their eyes. And the harder they tried to get out, the deeper they sank. What a time they had!

By the time they were out of it, Jack the Jumper was out of sight over the next Bare Ridge, and Shaggy and his friend sat down to howl their disappointment.

"Yow-oooooo," howled Shaggy, and "Yow-oooooo," howled his friend. They were both very hungry.

"Merry Christmas! Merry Christmas!" shouted Bud.

CHAPTER 18

"Merry Christmas"

"MERRY Christmas! Merry Christmas!" shouted Bud, as he opened the door to Mary's room and peeped in. But there was no Mary to be seen. "Now where do you suppose Sis is so early in the morning?"

Bud hurried back into his room and dressed. Then he ran down the Wide Stairway two steps at a time.

"Merry Christmas, sleepyhead!" laughed Mary; "it is a wonder you didn't sleep all day."

"It isn't late yet, is it?" said Bud.

"Only six o'clock, but that is late enough for Christmas morning," said Mary.

Out in the White Kitchen Mrs. Smith was preparing Christmas breakfast.

"Merry Christmas, Mother!" greeted Bud, and then the two children raced into the Cheery Parlor.

"Oh, what a beautiful Christmas Tree!" exclaimed Bud and Mary together, for right by the Broad Hearth was an Evergreen Tree, with its tinsel and decorations sparkling in the light from the Glowing Fireplace.

"Father and Mother always know how to fix it so pretty," said Mary.

Christmas Day was always a jolly time on the Old Homestead. Not that there were many expensive gifts given or much rich food to be eaten; oh, no, it wasn't that, for those things do not make a jolly Christmas. It was the spirit of the day that made everyone happy, and not the gifts they received—the spirit of peace and good will. The day was surely a merry one.

You see, although the Smiths observed Christmas Day, they did not do so with the thought that it really was Christ's Birthday, for they knew that no one knows exactly when the Christ Child was born. What the Smiths did on Christmas Day was to remember that Christ really had been born on *some day,* and to give praise and thanks to God for the gift of His only Son that all might have eternal life through Him. They thought that the gift of Jesus and of everlasting life was the most Perfect Gift that anyone could receive.

So as Mr. and Mrs. Smith and Bud and Mary knelt in the Cheery Parlor that morning, as they did every morning, they thanked the Heavenly Father for the many blessings they had received from Him during the past year, and especially for the Perfect Gift.

"What shall we do today?" asked Mary, after family worship was over.

"Let us make a Christmas Tree for the Feathered Friends," suggested Bud.

"Oh, that will be so much fun!" said Mary.

In a little while they were plodding through the Fleecy Snow across the Wide-Wide Pasture toward the Wood Lot. Nero the Hound had decided it would be interesting to go also, and he was running here and there and making Crooked Little Trails, and sniffing into every Warm Hollow Log and Friendly Burrow they passed.

Bud and Mary soon found an Evergreen Tree that suited them, and it was a short job for Bud to cut it down. Of course, they did not choose the nicest tree they could find, for they knew the Feathered Friends would not be looking at the tree but at what was on it.

Back across the Wide-Wide Pasture they trailed, carrying the Evergreen Tree. And there was Nero the Hound following along as if he were enjoying his part in it. Sometimes he would stop long enough to sniff in a Friendly Burrow to see if a Furry Friend was sound asleep in it. Then he would trot to catch up, and look up at Bud and Mary as much as to say: "Lazy Creatures, sleeping all winter!"

8—W. C.

Bud and Mary carried the Evergreen Tree to the Workshop, and there Bud made a frame to hold it up. Then they took it into the Cheery Parlor, where it was warmer, while they tied on presents for the birds.

"What shall we put on first?" asked Mary, when the Feathered Friends' Christmas Tree was ready to be decorated.

"Well, let's see," said Bud. "We can put on some cores from Flaming Red Apples for Cardinal the Grosbeak, for I know he will like the seeds in them as well as the apple. Next we can tie on some heads of Seedy Millet for Snowy the Bunting and Junco the Snowbird and others. Then we can run a string through some Yellow Pumpkin Seeds and hang them on, and pieces of Dry Bread Crust."

"We must not forget to take along some pieces of Suet for the Woodpeckers," said Mary.

"And some Mixed Grains for Bobby White and Ringneck the Pheasant and Hungarian the Partridge," added Bud.

Then Bud and Mary tied on some heads of Golden Wheat and Tame Sunflower and an ear of Pearly Corn for good measure.

"There, I guess everyone can find something that he likes on that Christmas Tree," said Bud. "We will take it out and tie it to a corner of the

Feeding Place so the Playful Air Whiffs cannot blow it over, and it will help to make a shelter for the Feathered Friends."

Bud and Mary carried the Evergreen Tree to the Feeding Place and fastened it so it would not blow over. Then they hid near by in a patch of Tame Currant Bushes, and watched.

Soon the Feathered Friends began to arrive from their Hiding Places and look for their Favorite Food on the Evergreen Tree.

"Oh, dear; we forgot to bring the Feathered Friends a drink," said Mary. "I must run right back and get some Warm Water for them."

That night Mr. and Mrs. Smith and Bud and Mary sat in front of the Glowing Fireplace. There was a basket of Flaming Red Apples and a dish of Delicious Nuts on a table, and Bud was popping Snowy Corn over the Glowing Fire. Over in the Black Forest, Shaggy the Wolf howled, "Yow-oooooo," and awoke the Little Wild Creatures as his voice echoed through the Wildwood Lanes.

"Bowwow," answered Nero the Hound, from the new house that Bud had made for him. "You had better not come near here."

"I think this has been the nicest Christmas that I can remember," said Mary.

"So do I," agreed Bud.

CHAPTER 19

Jim Crow the Tease

LIFE was rather dull for Jim Crow during the Wintry Weather. He could not find any Tender Corn Shoots to pull up. He could not find any Round Little Nests to rob of their eggs. And he could not even tease Screecher the Owl; Screecher was down in the Sunny Southland. Yes, sir; it certainly was a dull time. All Jim Crow could find to do was to fly across the Broad Fields from morning until night and "Caw-caw-caw." He did wish there was something interesting to do.

Sometimes Jim Crow went over to the Black Forest for a change, and then again he would visit in the Wood Lot. Of course he always took all his friends with him, for Jim never liked to be alone.

That is usually the way it is with anyone who is always into mischief. The one who is always getting into trouble is never satisfied unless he has someone with him. Perhaps it is because he wants someone to share the blame.

"Caw-caw-caw," said Jim Crow one Cold-Cold Day; "let's fly over to the Rustling Cornfield and eat some Tempting Kernels."

(116)

Jim liked to sit on the side of the Rustling Corn Shocks and pick Tempting Kernels from the ears that were sticking out.

Away flew Jim Crow and his friends, cawing and making a big fuss. They acted as if they thought they owned the Old Homestead.

After a while Jim Crow became tired of eating corn. He had eaten all he wanted.

"Caw-caw-caw," he said, "let's go to the Black Forest and see what our cousin Tattler the Jay is doing these Cold-Cold Days."

Now Tattler the Jay found things about as dull during Wintry Weather as Jim Crow did. Neither one was happy unless he was looking for mischief. But neither was their cousin Pesty the Magpie, for that matter. Tattler the Jay and Pesty the Magpie were bad enough, but Jim Crow was worse. He did not have a friend among the Little Wild Creatures. His reputation was as black as his coat, and that was pretty black.

When Jim Crow and his friends arrived at the Black Forest, they alighted on a Leafless Tree to look around. Then Jim flew over near a Great Pine Tree to see if Tattler the Jay was there; and whom do you suppose he saw? You never would guess. It was Snowy the Owl.

Snowy the Owl seldom came to the Old Home-

Away flew Jim Crow and his friends,
cawing and making a big fuss.

stead to visit. His home was in the Far-Far North
where Snowy the Bunting lived. Sometimes, when
the Fleecy Snow was deep and the Playful Air
Whiffs were very cold, Snowy the Owl came to
the Old Homestead in search of Snowshoe the
Hare and Drummer the Grouse and Whitetail the
Ptarmigan, as Blue Darter the Goshawk did.

And there he was sound asleep in that Great
Pine Tree when Jim Crow saw him. Snowy did
his hunting at night and slept during the day.
That was because he could see better at night.

Now if there was one thing that Jim Crow liked
to do better than another, it was to tease owls. He
thought nothing else was quite so much fun. He
had not been expecting to find an owl to tease.

"Caw-caw-caw," he said to his friends; "I have found Snowy the Owl hiding in this Great Pine Tree. What do you think of that?"

"Caw-caw-caw," said one of his friends; "let's play a game of Tease while Scrapper the Kingbird is in the Sunny Southland."

You see, Scrapper the Kingbird was one bird that Jim Crow and his friends were afraid of. Sometimes Scrapper would dart at them and pull out their black feathers; so they had to watch out for him. It seemed as if Scrapper was always sitting on a Lookout Stub where he could see them if they came anywhere near.

But during the Wintry Weather Scrapper lived in the Sunny Southland. So Jim Crow and his

Sometimes, when the Fleecy Snow was deep and the Playful Air Whiffs were very cold, Snowy the Owl came to the Old Homestead.

friends thought that would be a fine time to play a game of Tease with Snowy the Owl. They could hardly wait to begin.

"Caw-caw-caw," said one; and "Caw-caw-caw," said another.

Soon they were flying around and around and alighting in the Great Pine Tree near Snowy the Owl until Snowy was quite ruffed up about it. And who wouldn't object to being kept awake by so much noise? Oh, but Snowy was angry!

Now it happened that Terror the Hunter had come to the Black Forest with his Flashing Gun in search of Snowshoe the Hare. It seemed as if no one had so many Enemies as Snowshoe had. There were Great Horn the Owl and Shadow the Lynx and Snowy the Owl and Snoop the Weasel and Killer the Marten and many others besides Terror the Hunter.

But Snowshoe was well protected in his white coat. He was hidden under a Young Pine Tree that was almost covered with Fleecy Snow, and Terror had not found him.

"What do you suppose is the matter with Jim Crow?" said Terror to himself. "He seems to be making a loud noise about something."

Terror decided he would go over and see what mischief Jim Crow was up to.

Of course Jim Crow and his friends thought they were perfectly safe while Scrapper the King-bird was away. They were not thinking that Terror the Hunter might be in the Black Forest. So they were having a lot of fun teasing Snowy the Owl. Down through the Dense Timber sneaked Terror until he was quite near to Jim Crow and his friends.

"I believe I will take a shot and see how many crows I can kill," he said. "Boom," went his gun, and down fell two of Jim's friends.

Away flew Jim Crow and the others; and away flew Snowy the Owl also.

"Oh, I wish I had known Snowy was there!" said Terror, "for I do not get a chance to shoot at him very often."

CHAPTER 20

Tracks in the Snow

TRAILER the Mink was having quite a time to find anything to eat. He had hunted around the Duck Pond when Jack Frost first came. But in a little while the Duck Pond was covered with Glassy Ice, where Bud and Mary went skating. Then he had hunted along Little River. At last even Little River was frozen over, and then he had to fish under the ice; that is, if he fished at all.

But Trailer knew a trick that helped him to find something to eat even when the Fleecy Snow was deep on the ground and Little River was covered with Glassy Ice.

You see, right below Trailer's Hidden Den on the bank of Little River was a hole in the Glassy Ice. Trailer had made it himself. Whenever he wanted to go into the Icy Water, he always went in at the same place. Then the Glassy Ice could not freeze thick there.

Trailer would dive into the hole and break the Thin Little Crust, and then Old Man Winter would have to start all over again to freeze it. Then along would come Trailer and break it again. So

At last even Little River was frozen
over, and then Trailer had to fish through a hole in the ice.

Old Man Winter could not freeze any Glassy Ice
in that hole while Trailer the Mink was running
in and out of it so often.

But one day Trailer made a mistake. He went
over to the Duck Pond to hunt Jimmy the Swamp
Rabbit and didn't come back that day. While
he was away, Old Man Winter froze such a thick
door of Glassy Ice over the opening that Trailer
could not break through it; so Trailer was having
quite a time to find anything to eat.

Trailer started on a trip along Little River. He
thought he might catch a Feathered Friend in the
Jungle Thicket that grew along its banks. Or, he
thought, he might pounce on a Sleeping Bunny or
find the home of Tiny the Meadow Mouse.

At last he saw a Wide Crack in the Glassy Ice.

The Singing Water had grown lower and lower in Little River when the Bubbly Springs began to freeze in the High Mountains. And that left an empty space along the bank under the Glassy Ice.

Trailer the Mink dived into the Wide Crack and ran along under the Glassy Ice. Into the Singing Water he dived and came up with a Scaly Fish,—the best feast he had had in quite a while.

After Trailer had eaten his Scaly Fish, he ran along under the Glassy Ice until he came to another Wide Crack. Then he jumped up through it and ran along the bank in the Fleecy Snow.

"I believe I will go over to Paddletail the Beaver's Wildwood Pond and see if I can catch Danny Muskrat," said Trailer the Mink to himself.

Whitetail the Ptarmigan lived in the high mountains.

Trailer had to run here and there and sniff at every Friendly Burrow and Brush Pile he passed. And every place Trailer went he left a Crooked Little Trail in the Fleecy Snow.

Now it happened that Trailer the Mink was not the only one who had quite a time to find something to eat during Wintry Weather. Far up on the High Mountains was the home of Killer the Marten, and it is a mystery how he could find anything at all to eat up there.

It is true, Whitetail the Ptarmigan stayed there most of the time, and some of Snowshoe the Hare's friends were not far away. And there was Trader the Pack Rat.

One day Killer the Marten decided he would go hunting in the Black Forest. He thought he might find Snowshoe the Hare or Drummer the Grouse to feast upon. So down over the Deep Snowdrifts he went.

At last Killer the Marten reached the Black Forest and found the Bitter Willow Brush where Snowshoe the Hare lived. There were many, many Bunny Tracks and Sheltered Bunny Lanes among the Bitter Willow Bushes.

"Yum, yum!" thought Killer the Marten; "now I shall soon have a feast."

"Sniff, sniff," he went; "those smell like the

tracks of Trailer the Mink. I wonder what he is up to." Then Killer the Marten started to follow Trailer's tracks to find out.

But Killer the Marten did not know that Trailer the Mink had tried to catch Danny Muskrat, and that Danny and Mrs. Muskrat had swum away under the Glassy Ice and escaped, and that then Trailer had gone to the Bitter Willow Brush in search of Snowshoe the Hare.

So while Trailer the Mink was looking for Snowshoe the Hare, Killer the Marten was hunting Trailer. Down the Sheltered Bunny Lanes went Trailer's Crooked Little Trail, with Killer the Marten following everywhere it went.

How frightened Snowshoe would have been if he had known that Trailer the Mink and Killer the Marten were both in his Bitter Willow Brush! But there was Snowshoe sitting in his Cozy Form and thinking he was perfectly safe unless Shadow the Lynx came along.

You see, Killer the Marten almost never came down to the Black Forest, because he liked the High Mountains better. And Trailer the Mink did not come there often because he had so many other places to go. Trailer was a great traveler, and many times he was away from his Hidden Den for two weeks.

But, then, Killer the Marten was a traveler also. He was away from home so much that he scarcely knew where his real home was during Wintry Weather. He always went alone, and if he met another Marten, there was almost sure to be a fight. Although Killer the Marten was fierce, and would murder Trailer the Mink if he found him, he was better than Trailer in one way—he seldom killed more than he needed to eat. But Trailer the Mink would murder many, many more creatures than he could eat, solely for the fun of killing something.

CHAPTER 21

Fisher the Bold Goes Trailing

"WELL, well," said Fisher the Bold. "I do believe that these are Killer the Marten's tracks, and he is following Trailer the Mink. Now won't that be fun to go trailing after them?"

Fisher the Bold liked to travel as well as Killer the Marten and Trailer the Mink did; but that was not strange, because he was their cousin. Fisher the Bold was larger and fiercer than either of them. He could have killed Killer the Marten in a fair fight.

Fisher the Bold liked to hunt among the Tree-tops. He could run through the Springy Limbs faster than even Killer the Marten could, and that was very fast. Yes, sir, when Fisher the Bold started out to catch something, he fairly flew through the Treetops. And on the ground he could outrun Snowshoe the Hare.

Quite often Fisher the Bold wore Sharp Little Spears in his mouth and face, which Sticker the Porcupine had put there. It seemed as if Fisher the Bold had poor judgment, for he was always ready to pounce upon Sticker and his friends

There sat Snowshoe in his Cozy Form.

whenever he saw them. But for that matter, Fisher the Bold was not afraid to pounce upon Furry Friends that were much larger than he.

So, instead of only Trailer the Mink and Killer the Marten, poor Snowshoe the Hare had also Fisher the Bold in his Bitter Willow Bushes. And there he sat in his Cozy Form. It was a wonder that Shadow the Lynx was not there also, looking for him.

"I must hurry to see if I can catch Killer the Marten," said Fisher the Bold to himself.

"I must hurry and catch Trailer the Mink," thought Killer the Marten.

"I wonder where I can find Snowshoe the Hare," Trailer the Mink was asking himself.

So while Trailer the Mink ran up and down the Sheltered Bunny Lanes looking for Snowshoe the

Hare, Killer the Marten was trying his best to catch up with him. And there was Fisher the Bold hurrying to catch up with Killer the Marten.

Now the reason why everyone was in such a hurry was that the Gray Cloud Ships were sailing over and threatening to unload their Fleecy Snow any minute. That is what they started to do about the time the Laughing Yellow Sun should have been peeping out of the east.

Down came the Merry Little Snowflakes dancing and whirling into every Sheltered Bunny Lane. Soon they had found the Crooked Little Trail of Trailer the Mink and had filled every Scratchy Little Track that he had left. There wasn't a sign that Trailer had gone that way!

For a while Killer followed the direction that the Playful Air Whiffs told him Trailer had gone, but it did not take the Merry Little Snowflakes long to cover up the Familiar Scent.

"I think I shall have to find a Hiding Place and wait until the Merry Little Snowflakes stop tumbling down," said Killer the Marten to himself. Then he crawled into a Warm Hollow Log and went to sleep.

Of course the Merry Little Snowflakes also covered Killer the Marten's Scratchy Little Tracks and Fisher the Bold could no longer follow them.

"I see a Jumbled Rock Pile that will be a safe Hiding Place," said Fisher the Bold. "I shall sleep there until the Merry Little Snowflakes stop falling; then maybe I can find Killer the Marten."

Snowshoe the Hare sat in his Cozy Form and watched the Fleecy Snow grow deeper and deeper around his doorway. In a little while Snowshoe was covered with a Soft White Blanket. You never would have known he was there in his white coat.

After a while Snowshoe the Hare poked his head through the Soft White Blanket and peeped out. The Gray Cloud Ships had sailed on, leaving Fluffy White Mantles on the trees. The Laughing Yellow Sun was nodding good night behind the Treetops, and soon the Weird Darkness would creep out and chase away the Long Shadows.

Killer the Marten tried to find Trailer's Crooked Little Trail. But, sniff as hard as he might, he could not find it.

Snowshoe the Hare hopped out on the Fleecy Snow and looked around. "I believe I'll run over to the Big Jungle Thicket and eat some Wild Cherry Bark," he said.

Now when Trailer the Mink awoke, he did not like the idea of wading in the Fleecy Snow to find Snowshoe the Hare. And so away he went down Little River toward his own Hidden Den. He would rather find a Wide Crack in the Glassy Ice and then hunt under the Glassy Ice as he had done at other times.

Killer the Marten came out of the Warm Hollow Log and tried to find Trailer the Mink's Crooked Little Trail. But sniff as hard as he might he could not find it.

"I suppose I may as well go back to the High Mountains and see if I can find Whitetail the Ptarmigan," he said; "but I do wish I could have found Trailer the Mink." He would have been fully as pleased to catch Snowshoe the Hare.

Fisher the Bold was not in good humor when he came out of his Jumbled Rock Pile and saw that all the Sheltered Bunny Lanes were filled with Fleecy Snow. But it did not take him long to find the Crooked Little Trail that Killer the Marten had left when he started back toward the High Mountains.

"Well, well, I see that Killer the Marten is out already," said Fisher the Bold. "I know it will be easy to catch him in this deep Fleecy Snow."

Away went Fisher the Bold as fast as he could run, leaving another Crooked Little Trail with the one that Killer the Marten had left. Now who do you suppose saw those Crooked Little Trails the next morning?

The Black Forest was crossed with Crooked Little Trails.

Chapter 22

Trapper Jim Looks for Signs

WELL, sir, it was Trapper Jim who saw those Crooked Little Trails the next day. You see, when he went to bed about the time that Killer the Marten and Fisher the Bold started for the High Mountains, the Gray Cloud Ships had sailed on and the Merry Little Snowflakes were no longer falling.

"Tomorrow I shall take my traps and go out to look for Crooked Little Trails," said Trapper Jim to himself.

Trapper Jim knew that during the night the Furry Friends would be out making Crooked Little Trails everywhere in the new Fleecy Snow. He knew that if he could find their Crooked Little Trails he could set traps for them.

So, bright and early, Trapper Jim put on his Webby Snowshoes and started out across the White Fields, carrying a bunch of traps. Shortly before he came to the Old Homestead, Trapper Jim turned off and went toward the Black Forest.

Farmer Smith did not want anyone to set traps on the Old Homestead unless it was necessary. Of course if Reddy Fox or Shaggy the Wolf or Snoop the Weasel or some of the other Furbearers became too bold and caught some of Old Cluck's Chicklets, then something had to be done about it; and traps were set.

But Farmer Smith did not think it was right to make the Furbearers suffer, and to take their lives, merely to get their Silky Fur to wear. He knew that some of the Furbearers like Spot the Skunk and his cousin Mephitis the Skunk were his friends and helped to keep the Fat Grasshoppers and Plump Grubs and Whiskers the Mouse from destroying his crops.

Trapper Jim knew that Farmer Smith did not allow any trapping on the Old Homestead; that was why he turned toward the Black Forest. It seemed as if many of the Furbearers that lived on the Old Homestead were asleep anyway, such as Digger the Badger and Mephitis the Skunk and Billy Coon.

But most of the Furbearers that lived in the Black Forest, like Killer the Marten and Fisher the Bold and Shadow the Lynx and Shaggy the Wolf, did not mind the Wintry Weather at all. Trapper Jim knew that in the Black Forest was a good place to look for their Crooked Little Trails.

Just before Trapper Jim reached the Black Forest, he turned toward Little River. He thought he might see the Crooked Little Trail of Trailer the Mink, because he knew that Trailer liked to go visiting along Little River.

Sure enough, there was Trailer's Crooked Little Trail as plain as anything; and there was the Wide Crack in the Glassy Ice where he had gone under it.

"Ha-ha," laughed Trapper Jim; "here's the place to set a trap. Then the next time Trailer comes this way he will jump right into it."

Trapper Jim set one of his traps and placed it right under the Wide Crack where Trailer's foot would strike it if he jumped down in there again. Then Trapper Jim went on his way toward the Black Forest.

"Ha-ha," he laughed, "if here isn't the Crooked Little Trail of Killer the Marten, and I see that Fisher the Bold is following him. I shall see where they are going."

So along the Crooked Little Trails went Trapper Jim. Every little way he would stop and set a trap and then leave a Tempting Bait beside it. He thought that if Killer the Marten or Fisher the Bold or Shadow the Lynx went by that way, the Playful Air Whiffs would tell them about the Tempting Baits. Then when they came to the

Carcajou the Glutton was the largest and fiercest in the Weasel family. He was always ready to eat.

Tempting Baits, they would walk right into the traps he had set for them. They would be so hungry they would never think of traps at all.

"Well, I think I may as well go home," said Trapper Jim, when he had set his last trap. "Tomorrow I shall be sure to have a nice catch of Furbearers."

But that was once when Trapper Jim was mistaken; and it all happened like this:

Killer the Marten and Fisher the Bold had a cousin. His name was Carcajou the Glutton. Carcajou was much larger than either of them, and he was very fierce. He was so fierce that he was sometimes called Wolverine the Terrible. The Indians were the first to call him Carcajou, because that was their way of saying "devil." He was the

(138)

largest and fiercest in the Weasel family, and Snoop was the smallest.

Now if there was one thing that Carcajou liked to do better than anything else, it was to eat. It seemed as if he was always ready to eat. Sometimes we see people who are like that, and we call them "gluttons." Carcajou the Glutton was always hungry, and he was always in a ferocious mood. He was always cross.

One day Carcajou the Glutton was walking through the Black Forest. He was looking for something to eat, as usual. Sometimes Sneak the Cougar would kill one of Lightfoot the Deer's friends and eat only a part of it. Then Carcajou would come along and finish it. He would have a feast while Growler the Bear was asleep in his Warm Dark Cave and could not find it first. He was looking for something like that in the Black Forest.

Suddenly Carcajou saw a Snowshoe Trail in the Fleecy Snow. It was the Snowshoe Trail that Trapper Jim had made.

"Now I wonder if Trapper Jim has been setting traps in the Black Forest and has left some Tempting Baits," thought Carcajou the Glutton. And then he went over to find out what that Snowshoe Trail was all about.

"Sniff, sniff," went Carcajou; "yes, it surely was Trapper Jim who made this Snowshoe Trail; I smell the Sweet-Smelling Lure that he dragged behind him to get the Furbearers to follow him to his traps."

Carcajou the Glutton was very wise. He had a keen nose, and he could tell where every trap was set. So he followed the Snowshoe Trail and ate all the Tempting Baits that Trapper Jim had left, and spoiled the sets as he went. Then he went back to his home in the High Mountains.

Wasn't Trapper Jim angry when he saw what Carcajou had done! for, of course, he could not catch the Furbearers after Carcajou had spoiled the sets.

CHAPTER 23

Lightfoot the Deer Makes a Move

LIGHTFOOT the Deer had been living in the Big Jungle Thicket in the Black Forest. Lightfoot liked the Big Jungle Thicket because he could hide in it, and he could also find plenty to eat there. He did not care for grass to eat, so it made no difference to him if it was covered with Fleecy Snow. What Lightfoot liked to eat was Tender Buds and Savory Twigs and such things. And he could find all he wanted even though there was much Fleecy Snow.

Now Lightfoot the Deer had a Great Enemy. That was Sneak the Cougar. Sneak would sit on the limbs of trees during the Balmy Summer Days and wait for Lightfoot or his friends to walk under, and then he would pounce upon them.

For a long time Sneak had been wondering what had become·of Lightfoot. You see, when the first Merry Little Snowflakes fell and covered the ground, Lightfoot had gone to the Big Jungle Thicket and lived there. He did not care to wade through the Fleecy Snow and leave a Crooked Little Trail for Sneak to follow. No, sir; he hid in the Big Jungle Thicket; and Sneak did not know where to find him.

One day Pesty the Magpie was flying through the Big Jungle Thicket and saw Lightfoot the Deer. Pesty was very hungry, and he was wondering where he could find something to eat.

"I know what I'll do," said Pesty; "I'll tell Sneak the Cougar where Lightfoot is; and then when Sneak pounces upon Lightfoot, I'll have a feast." Away went Pesty the Magpie to look for Sneak the Cougar.

Naturally, Sneak was glad to know where to find Lightfoot. That very night he went sneaking through the Blackberry Brambles and Twining Vines in search of him. But although Sneak was careful not to make any noise, some friends told Lightfoot that Sneak was coming. They were the Playful Air Whiffs that came stealing through the Wildwood Lanes straight to Lightfoot's nose.

"Sniff, sniff," went Lightfoot; "I smell Sneak the Cougar. I fear that he has found my Hiding Place at last. I'll go over to the Little Jungle Thicket at the foot of High Cliff where Molly and Peter Cottontail live, and stay there."

Away ran Lightfoot through the Fleecy Snow with his funny stiff-legged jumps, over Stubby Bushes and through Blackberry Brambles. Oh,

How disappointed Sneak the Cougar was when
he could not find Lightfoot in the Big Jungle Thicket!

how disappointed Sneak the Cougar was when
he could not find Lightfoot in the Big Jungle
Thicket!

Sometimes the Wild Creatures fear one another so much that they almost forget to be afraid
of Fearful the Man. They come to him for protec-
tion when their Wild Enemies seek their lives.
They seem to know that he will care for them.

That was the way it was with Lightfoot the
Deer. When he knew that Sneak the Cougar had
found him, and that Sneak was waiting for a
chance to pounce upon him, Lightfoot thought he
would move nearer to the Old Homestead where
Sneak would be afraid to come. That was why he
went to the Little Jungle Thicket at the foot of

High Cliff to live until Jolly Spring came and
chased away the Fleecy Snow. Then Lightfoot
would not leave a Crooked Little Trail that Sneak
could follow.

One day Bud started to the Wood Lot to look
around. He liked to walk through the Fleecy
Snow among the Leafless Trees and see how many
Feathered Friends he could count. He thought he
might see Chatterer the Red Squirrel and Worker
the Gray Squirrel going to their Secret Storehouses
after Favorite Food.

As Bud was passing the Little Jungle Thicket,
he thought he saw a Crooked Little Trail going
into it.

"Surely Old Bent Horn could not have escaped
from the Big Corral by the Rambling Old Barn,"
thought Bud. And then he was near enough to
see that the Crooked Little Trail was much
smaller than Old Bent Horn would have made.

Suddenly there was the sound of running feet,
and Bud spied Lightfoot the Deer jumping back
into the Little Jungle Thicket.

"Well, well, if it isn't Lightfoot!" he exclaimed.
"Now what do you suppose he is doing here? I
wonder if he wouldn't like some Dried Clover
Leaves to eat these Cold-Cold Days. I'll give him
some right now."

Back to the Rambling Old Barn went Bud. He knew that in the haymow were many, many Dried Clover Leaves that had fallen off when Farmer Smith was throwing down hay to Old Sorrel. It did not take Bud long to fill a sack with them, and soon he was carrying it toward the Little Jungle Thicket.

"I hope that Lightfoot finds these Dried Clover Leaves," said Bud, as he emptied the sack in a Little Open Space that was hidden in the Little Jungle Thicket.

Now it happened that Molly and Peter were very, very hungry. The Fleecy Snow had covered the ground a long time, and they could not find any Tender Grass Shoots to eat. They had nib-

Suddenly there was the sound of running feet, and Bud spied Lightfoot the Deer jumping back into the Little Jungle Thicket.

bled the Spicy Bark from some Wild Cherry Trees, and had eaten Tender Buds when they could find some. Once Molly went to the Apple Orchard and chewed some Spicy Bark from one of Farmer Smith's Apple Trees.

That was not a nice thing to do, of course, but Molly was very hungry. And, besides, Molly did not know that she was doing wrong.

Molly and Peter came out of their Friendly Burrow and sat there wondering where to go to find something to eat.

"If we were down along Little River, we could find some Tart Grapevines," said Molly.

Peter wiggled his nose and sat up. "It seems to me that I can smell Dried Clover Leaves; though I don't know how they could get here," he said.

Molly hopped down a Sheltered Bunny Lane a way. "I do smell Dried Clover Leaves!" she said; and, what is more, I see them. Bud Smith must have brought them over here for us."

Then Molly and Peter had a feast, but there were plenty left for Lightfoot. And Bud brought some more to the Little Jungle Thicket.

CHAPTER 24

Shadow the Lynx Is Fooled

SHADOW the Lynx was a small cousin of Sneak the Cougar. He lived in the Black Forest, and sometimes he went to the High Mountains hunting. He liked to hunt in the Jungle Thickets along Little River, and the one he liked best was the Bitter Willow Bushes where Snowshoe the Hare lived most of the time.

The reason why Shadow the Lynx liked that place best was that he liked to hunt Snowshoe the Hare and his friends. There simply was not anything that Shadow liked better to eat than fresh rabbit meat.

In the Wintry Weather, Shadow wore large, hairy pads on his feet, and they helped him to walk on the Fleecy Snow. He could walk on it about as well as Snowshoe the Hare could, with his large feet.

When Trapper Jim wanted to walk on the Fleecy Snow, he had to put on Webby Snowshoes that looked something like tennis rackets, but they were many times larger. Sometimes Trapper Jim wore a Ski on each foot that looked like a long, narrow toboggan. They made it easier to walk.

Trapper Jim was one Great Enemy that Shadow feared. You see, sometimes Trapper Jim went through the Black Forest setting traps for Furbearers. Trapper Jim knew that Snowshoe the Hare liked to stay in the Bitter Willow Bushes where he could nibble their Spicy Bark. And Trapper Jim knew that Shadow the Lynx liked to stay where he could hunt Snowshoe the Hare. Therefore he knew that Shadow stayed in the Bitter Willow Bushes much of the time.

Now, while Trapper Jim set traps for most of the Furbearers, he had a special way to catch Shadow's friends. That was with Snares. The Bible says that Satan sets snares to catch us, but, of course, they are not the kind that Trapper Jim used. Satan's snares are little temptations, which finally bind us with bad habits if we do not see them and avoid them.

The kind of Snares that Trapper Jim set for Shadow the Lynx were made of strong cord. They had large loops in them. Trapper Jim made Cubby Pens with doors in which he hung the loops. Then he put a Tempting Bait in the back of the pen to coax Shadow to put his head through the loop. If Shadow was not watching, the loop would tighten around his neck, and then he could not get away unless he broke the strong cord.

Satan places little temptations like Tempting Baits in our way so we will get caught by habit snares, and then the only way we can escape is to break the habit snares. Sometimes they are so strong that we need strength from Jesus to help us to break them. He will always help us when we ask Him.

One night Shadow the Lynx went hunting down along Little River. First he passed Paddletail the Beaver's Wildwood Pond, which was covered with Glassy Ice, and then he hunted in some of the Jungle Thickets along the banks of Little River. After a while he came to the edge of the Black Forest; but there were still more Jungle Thickets along Little River; so Shadow went on.

At last Shadow came to the place where Little River went near the Grand Old House, and he was afraid that Nero the Hound would smell him if he kept going.

"I believe I will go over to the Little Jungle Thicket and see if I can catch Molly Cottontail," said Shadow, for it was almost time for the Laughing Yellow Sun to wink good morning. "Yes, sir; I can look for Molly, and then I can hide there until the Weird Darkness comes again."

Most of the time when Loxia the Cross-bill was visiting on the Old Homestead, he lived in the Black Forest.

Shadow knew that he could not get back to the Black Forest before the Laughing Yellow Sun would catch him, so he hurried to the Little Jungle Thicket where Molly and Peter Cottontail lived in their Friendly Burrow.

It was quite light when Shadow arrived at the Little Jungle Thicket, and he thought it was time to hunt a Hiding Place and go to sleep. So he started to sneak back into a clump of Low Cedar Trees near a Little Open Space, when right there before his eyes he saw Peter and Molly Cottontail eating the Dried Clover Leaves that Bud had brought!

"Now isn't that luck!" thought Shadow the Lynx. "I surely will have fresh rabbit meat for supper." And then he started to sneak a little closer so he could easily pounce upon Molly.

(150)

Now it happened that there was a queer-looking visitor staying on the Old Homestead during the Wintry Weather. At least he had a queer-looking bill. Instead of meeting squarely, as one would think all well-arranged bills should meet, his upper and lower bills crossed at the end almost like the heavy nippers that Farmer Smith used when he trimmed his trees.

In case you have not guessed this Feathered Friend's name, I will tell you. It is Loxia the Crossbill.

Loxia the Crossbill seldom came to the Old Homestead. His home was in the land of Cold Breezes, and he came to visit the Old Homestead only when Old Man Winter was too severe in his own land.

Most of the time when Loxia was visiting on the Old Homestead, he lived in the Black Forest. The reason for that was, he was very fond of Delicious Pine Cones. "Snip, snip," he would go, with his queer-looking crossed bill, and out would fall the Nut Meats from the inside as if his bill were made for doing that very thing.

When Shadow the Lynx arrived at the Little Jungle Thicket, Loxia the Crossbill was beginning to eat his breakfast. "Snip, snip," he went on a Delicious Pine Cone; "snip, snip, snip, snip."

Soon he had eaten all he wanted from that Delicious Pine Cone, and down it dropped almost on Molly's head.

Thumptey, thumpety, thump, went Molly and Peter, as they ran for their Friendly Burrow, leaving Shadow the Lynx sitting there.

"Now who do you suppose threw that rock at us?" asked Molly, as they dived out of sight.

CHAPTER 25

Billy Coon Takes a Stroll

"OH, dear, I feel all cramped up," said Billy Coon. "I believe I shall go for a walk." Billy Coon had been asleep in his Hollow Den Tree by the Bridge that crossed Little River. It was no wonder that he felt cramped, for he had been asleep almost a month.

You see, if the Wintry Weather was not too cold, Billy Coon did not sleep long at a time. He was not like Johnny Chuck. But sometimes when the Wintry Weather was very, very cold and there was much Fleecy Snow on the ground, Billy Coon would curl up and go to sleep until it was warmer again.

When Billy Coon peeped out of his Hollow Den Tree, the Smiling Moon seemed to wink at him and say, "Come on out; it is going to be a grand night."

Billy stepped out on the Big Limb that was his front porch and looked around. It surely was a nice, warm night. Almost all the Fleecy Snow was gone, and the Glassy Ice along Little River had melted in places.

"I wonder if I could find some Dried Berries in the Jungle Thickets along Little River," thought Billy, as he slid down his Hollow Den Tree.

In a little while he was pushing through the Pussy Willows and Blackberry Brambles and Twining Vines. He found a few Dried Grapes hanging from a Tart Grapevine, which the Feathered Friends had not seen.

"I fear that the Feathered Friends have eaten most of the Dried Berries," complained Billy Coon. "But I know what I shall do. I'll go to the Rustling Cornfield and eat some Tempting Kernels."

Now Billy Coon did not know that Farmer Smith had hauled away all the Rustling Corn Shocks. You see, while the Fleecy Snow was deep, he had needed them to feed to Old Bent Horn. So he had hauled away every one on a Slidy Sled. He had even taken the one under which Tiny the Meadow Mouse had dug his Friendly Burrow and had made his Soft Little Nest.

But Tiny did not care much, for he had made a Secret Storehouse in his Friendly Burrow and had filled it with Tempting Kernels before Farmer Smith took away the Rustling Corn Shock. Tiny the Meadow Mouse would have liked it better if Farmer Smith had left the Rust-

Billy Coon peeped out of his Hollow Den Tree, and the Smiling Moon seemed to wink at him.

ling Corn Shock so he would have had a better place to play, but Tiny would be moving to the Green Meadow when nice weather came, so it really did not matter.

There was one place that Billy Coon liked to visit almost as well as the Jungle Thicket along Little River, and that was the Wood Lot. He had explored it many, many times; but every time he went there he found something new. Of course Billy could not miss such a good chance to go there.

"I will see what I can find in the Wood Lot on my way to the Rustling Cornfield," said Billy. "I really haven't visited there for a long time."

One thing that attracted Billy Coon to the Wood Lot was the Sweet Nuts that grew there.

But between Bud Smith and Tawny Chipmunk and Chatterer the Red Squirrel and Worker the Gray Squirrel there were not many Sweet Nuts left for Billy Coon, although he could sometimes find a few that the others had missed. Then what a feast of Sweet Nuts Billy Coon had!

But Billy Coon was not always that fortunate. Usually he had to hunt and hunt, and especially toward the end of the Wintry Weather after everyone had taken all the Sweet Nuts he could find.

So when Billy Coon arrived at the Wood Lot, he found that the Sweet Nuts were very scarce. Yes, sir; he hunted and hunted, and he could not find a single one. There may have been some hiding

Chatterer had been in such a hurry that he had not covered the Sweet Nuts well.

under the patches of Fleecy Snow, but Billy Coon could not find them.

"I may as well go on to the Rustling Cornfield and eat some Tempting Kernels," he said.

And then, when Billy Coon was ready to leave, he made a discovery. Right by an Old Stump, and partly covered with decayed wood, was a pile of Sweet Nuts.

"Now who do you suppose hid those there?" said Billy Coon. "I will eat a few before I go to the Rustling Cornfield."

Now it happened that one day when Chatterer the Red Squirrel was exploring in the Wood Lot, he found one of Worker the Gray Squirrel's Secret Storehouses. It did not take Chatterer long to decide that he would steal some of Worker's Sweet Nuts. So away he went with as many as he could carry, and he buried them by the Old Stump. Again and again he visited Worker's Secret Storehouse until he had taken the very last Sweet Nut from it.

Chatterer had been in such a hurry that he had not covered the Sweet Nuts well, and Billy Coon had found them. And there was Billy Coon eating the Sweet Nuts that Chatterer had stolen from Worker. I think that was a good joke on Chatterer, don't you?

After a while Billy Coon went on to the Rustling Cornfield. He thought he would eat some Tempting Kernels to finish his meal. But when he arrived at the Rustling Cornfield he saw that every Rustling Corn Shock was gone. So by the time he had looked around for some Scattered Ears, it was almost time for the Laughing Yellow Sun to chase away the Weird Darkness.

"Oh, dear, I must find a place to sleep, for I cannot reach the Hollow Den Tree before it is light!" said Billy.

Billy saw a Hidden Den that was large enough for him to crawl into, and in he went. But he was glad to back right out again, for the Hidden Den belonged to Digger the Badger, and Digger was at home. Then Billy Coon had to crawl into the top of a Squatty Haystack and curl up for a snooze.

CHAPTER 26

Digger the Badger Hunts Dodger the Gopher

NOT far from the Hollow Den Tree where Chatterer the Red Squirrel lived in the Wood Lot was the Friendly Burrow of Dodger the Gopher. Dodger's Friendly Burrow was in the edge of the Wide-Wide Pasture right by the Wood Lot.

Dodger the Gopher was a queer fellow. During the Wintry Weather he sometimes slept as much as half a year without waking. During the fall days he ate and ate and grew fatter and fatter. Then when the Fleecy Snow came, he curled up in his Friendly Burrow like a furry ball and went to sleep. It was a wonder that he knew when it was time to awake.

Dodger the Gopher was a near relative of Chatterer the Red Squirrel and Worker the Gray Squirrel. Sometimes Dodger was called a "striped gopher," but he was really a ground squirrel.

Dodger liked to eat the same things that the other squirrels ate, but he was not like his cousins when it came to sleeping. Worker and Chatterer

Sometimes Dodger was called a "striped gopher," but he was really a ground squirrel.

did not sleep all winter as Dodger did. Sometimes on real Cold-Cold Days Worker the Gray Squirrel stayed in his Big Stick Nest days at a time, but Chatterer the Red Squirrel never seemed to think it was too cold for him. Chatterer really enjoyed scurrying around in the snow.

Dodger liked to live where the grass was not too high in the Wide-Wide Pasture. He liked short grass so that when he sat up on his hind feet he could see if an Enemy was near. Usually he cut the grass around his Friendly Burrow and carried it inside for a Snug Bed. Sometimes he put it in his Secret Storehouse to eat. For even though Dodger the Gopher slept during Wintry Weather, still he gathered a supply of Tempting Kernels

and Grass and Sweet Nuts as Worker the Gray
Squirrel did.

Perhaps Dodger could sleep better if he knew
that he had a good breakfast waiting for him when
he awoke. At least he liked to have some Favorite
Food handy for Stormy Spring Days. So he had
made a Secret Storehouse in his Friendly Burrow.
Sometimes he used two or more rooms in which
to store his food.

Yes, sir; it was a wonder that Dodger the
Gopher knew when to wake up after sleeping so
long. But one day something told him it was time
to leave his Snug Bed. Perhaps it was the Bright
Little Sunbeams, for when Dodger peeped out of
his Friendly Burrow, they had melted all the
Fleecy Snow. The Merry Little Snowflakes would
probably fall again sometimes before Jolly Spring
came back to stay; but when Dodger first awoke
after sleeping so long, it looked as if Old Man
Winter was ready to leave. The Bright Little Sunbeams were everywhere.

In a few days Dodger noticed that all the Favorite Food in his Secret Storehouse was gone. He
had eaten every bit of it, and he wondered where
he could find some more.

Suddenly Dodger remembered the Rustling
Cornfield. He had been there the fall before and

11—W. C.

had brought back some sacks of Tempting Kernels.

Did you know that Dodger has sacks in which to carry his supplies? Well, he has. On each side of his face he has a large pouch, and he uses these pouches for sacks in which to carry things.

Dodger liked Tempting Kernels to eat better than almost anything else, and they were handy to carry in his sacks. But there were none near his Friendly Burrow. The nearest Tempting Kernels were in the Rustling Cornfield, and that was clear across the Wide-Wide Pasture.

Dodger did not know whether to risk going that far or not. He was afraid that an Enemy might see him. He had a great many Enemies who would be glad to pounce upon him if they had a chance. Even Forktongue the Snake watched for Dodger on Balmy Summer Days. So Dodger seldom went far from his Friendly Burrow.

But Dodger wanted some Tempting Kernels very much. "I believe I will go and fill my Cheek Sacks with Tempting Kernels and bring them back to my Friendly Burrow to eat," he said.

When Dodger reached the Rustling Cornfield, he had a hard time to find a Scattered Ear. But at last he found one and stuffed his Cheek Sacks as

Digger the Badger burrowed into the Soft Earth expecting every minute to catch Dodger.

full as they could be. Suddenly Dodger looked up, and there, not more than two rabbit jumps away, was Digger the Badger coming after him.

Of course it was more than two jumps for Digger the Badger with his short legs and wide, fat back. And it was many jumps for Dodger. How Dodger did run! He ran as fast as he could with his Cheek Sacks sticking out full of corn. He dodged into the first Friendly Burrow he came to, and not a bit too soon, for right after him he heard Digger's Long Toenails tearing up the ground.

Dodger had not been in that Friendly Burrow before. It was an old one, and it was partly filled with trash. It kept Dodger busy cleaning the Secret Little Tunnel as he went. And there was

Digger making the dirt fly right behind him. Once Dodger ran into a side Secret Little Tunnel that came to an end, and Digger almost caught him before he could run back and find the right one.

At last Dodger found a Secret Little Tunnel leading upward, and almost before he knew it he was again above ground. That was a lucky find for Dodger.

So while Digger the Badger burrowed into the Soft Earth expecting every minute to catch Dodger the Gopher, there was Dodger hurrying home to his own Friendly Burrow as fast as he could go, with his Cheek Sacks still full of Tempting Kernels. But then, that was good exercise for Digger, for he had been asleep during the Cold-Cold Days.

If Digger the Badger did not make so many holes in the Wide-Wide Pasture for Old Sorrel and Old Bent Horn to step into, he would not be a bad citizen; but he does like to dig.

Chapter 27

Downy the Woodpecker Starts a Race

OVER in the Black Forest all the Wild Creatures were happy. The Laughing Yellow Sun had melted all the Fleecy Snow, and he had even warmed the Playful Air Whiffs enough so that they could steal into the Shadows and melt the Fleecy Snow there. And there was not a piece of Glassy Ice left.

It looked as if Jolly Spring was about ready to arrive and drive Old Man Winter back to his home in the Land of Ice.

Of course, as soon as the Laughing Yellow Sun sank from sight behind the Black Forest and the Weird Darkness chased away the Long Shadows, Jack Frost would steal along the Wildwood Pond and freeze a rim of Glassy Ice, and make all kinds of fancywork on the Dead Grass and Tumbled Bulrushes.

Oh, how glad Paddletail the Beaver and Danny Muskrat were! It had been such a long time since they could play Dive and Spin and Water Tag together. But even yet, Jack Frost would freeze Sharp Little Icicles on their Glossy Fur if they

Whitebreast hung with his head downward while he tore off some more Tiny Bark Chips.

stayed out of the water for too long a period.

Besides Paddletail the Beaver and Danny Muskrat, there were two others in the Black Forest who were glad to see the Fleecy Snow leave. They were Downy the Woodpecker and Whitebreast the Nuthatch. There were others also besides Downy and Whitebreast, but Downy and Whitebreast were especially glad.

You see, it was sometimes hard to find Tree Borers and Plump Grubs while the trees were covered with Fleecy Snow. Once Whitebreast had actually slid off a tree trunk that was covered with Glassy Ice. But when the Playful Air Whiffs grew warmer, there were more Crawly Bark Lice and such things to find. Downy the Woodpecker and

Whitebreast the Nuthatch had been thankful for the many Goodies that Bud Smith had kept for them at the Feeding Place in the Apple Orchard. But it was more fun to hunt for Favorite Food in the Black Forest.

Now it happened that one day Whitebreast the Nuthatch was hunting Tree Borers in the Black Forest.

"Rip-rip, rip-rip-rip," he went with his sharp bill, and made the Tiny Bark Chips fly. Soon he reached in and pulled out a Plump Grub.

"Tap-tap-tap-tap," went someone near by. It was Downy drilling in the rough bark. In a moment Downy reached in with his needlelike tongue and speared a Tree Borer.

"Rip-rip, rip-rip-rip," went Whitebreast again, and out came another Plump Grub.

"You seem to be busy this morning," said Downy to Whitebreast. "How would you like to run a race?"

Whitebreast hung with his head downward while he tore off some more Tiny Bark Chips. He could work as well with his head down as up, for he never braced himself with his tail as Downy did when he was hanging on the side of a tree.

"Yes, I am always busy," said Whitebreast; "but I think it would be fun to have a race."

Browny liked to hunt for Crawly Bark Lice.

"Oh, let me race too," said Browny the Creeper. "I am sure I can win."

So Downy the Woodpecker and Whitebreast the Nuthatch and Browny the Creeper started out to see who could catch the most Tree Borers and Plump Grubs and Crawly Bark Lice.

Now, although Downy and Whitebreast and Browny all liked to hunt among the trees, yet they were not related, as one might suppose. You see, Downy was related to Redhead the Woodpecker and Judge Flicker and others of the Woodpecker family. It really was quite a large family.

One of them lived in the Far-Far North and had only three toes on each foot. He was Mr. Arctic Three-Toed Woodpecker, and he wore two of his toes in front and one behind on each foot so he could cling to the sides of trees.

Another of Downy's cousins was Mr. California Woodpecker. He had a queer habit of drilling holes in trees and buildings and other places, barely large enough to hold a Sweet Nut or Sweet Acorn, and then he would hide one in each hole. He must have been playing the game of Pretend, and was pretending that he was a squirrel.

Sometimes Mr. Arctic Three-Toed Woodpecker came to the Old Homestead on a visit, but Mr. California Woodpecker never came. Downy was the smallest of the Woodpecker family.

Whitebreast the Nuthatch was Dandy the Chickadee's cousin and belonged to a different family than the Woodpeckers, while Browny the Creeper belonged to a still different family called Tree Creepers.

You may be sure that when Downy and Whitebreast and Browny started on their race, it was time for the Tree Borers and Plump Grubs and Crawly Bark Lice to keep out of sight. And a hard time they had with Downy and Whitebreast and Browny each hunting in a different way.

There was Downy flying from tree to tree and spearing into little holes with his sharp tongue, while he braced himself with his tail. And there was Whitebreast running headfirst down the trees and looking for Tree Borers from above.

Browny the Creeper started at the bottom of the trees and ran up and round and round, while he watched for Crawly Bark Lice. Browny liked to hunt for Crawly Bark Lice, because his bill was hardly strong enough to rip open the bark after Plump Grubs.

Now, it would be hard to say which one would have won the race if nothing had happened. But here came Redhead the Woodpecker and Judge Flicker and Dandy the Chickadee all hunting for Tree Borers and Plump Grubs and Crawly Bark Lice, and in a little while they were all so busy that they completely forgot to watch what the others were doing.

It was an interesting race, indeed, and we think that Whitebreast won because he could do more tricks on the sides of trees.

CHAPTER 28

Tawny Chipmunk Wakes Up

TAWNY CHIPMUNK had been sleeping all winter in his Hidden Den under a big rock not far from where Johnny Chuck had been sleeping. Their Hidden Dens were on the side of High Cliff not far from the Little Jungle Thicket where Molly and Peter lived in their Friendly Burrow.

Tawny Chipmunk had slept at least five months. I should think that he would have been rested after sleeping so long, wouldn't you? But when Tawny Chipmunk awoke, what do you suppose he did the first thing? Well, sir, he climbed up a Leafless Tree, stretched out on a Springy Limb where the Bright Little Sunbeams could warm his back, and went to sleep.

It may have been that the Bright Little Sunbeams hurt Tawny's eyes after he had slept so long in the dark, and he was waiting for them to become accustomed to the light. And then, again, maybe he was waiting for the Warm Sunshine to limber his legs after they had been still so long. Tawny Chipmunk surely did like Warm Sunshine!

Sometimes when the Gray Cloud Ships hid the Laughing Yellow Sun, Tawny stayed in his Hidden Den all day. He didn't care much about coming out unless there were Bright Little Sunbeams to warm his back.

At last he stretched himself and sat up on the Springy Limb. Tawny could sit on a limb as well as Worker the Gray Squirrel could, and it was no wonder, because he was a distant relative. Tawny was also related to Dodger the Gopher, and he looked much more like Dodger than he looked like Worker. Tawny had many, many relatives. Some of them slept during the Wintry Weather and some did not.

"I wonder if there are any Pussy Willow Buds

Tawny had to be very careful because he had so many Enemies.

There was Snoop the Weasel sneaking
up to catch Molly.

down along Little River," thought Tawny Chipmunk. "I do like Silky Little Buds."

Now, Tawny Chipmunk had plenty of Tiny
Little Seeds and Tempting Kernels and other Favorite Food in his Secret Storehouse, but he was
hungry for something else. Before Old Man Winter came, Tawny had gathered many Cheek Sacks
full of Favorite Food and had put it in his Secret
Storehouse, a separate room in his Hidden Den.
But Tawny liked to keep his supply of Favorite
Food for stormy and cloudy days when he did not
care to come out and look for more.

So Tawny decided that he would go down to
Little River and see if there were any Pussy Willow Buds. It may have been that one reason why

(173)

Tawny wanted some Silky Little Buds to eat was to start his lazy stomach to work after it had been resting all winter. Then, again, it may have been that Tawny wanted to stretch his legs after being idle so long.

Tawny had to be very careful whenever he went anywhere, because he had so many Enemies. He had even more Enemies than Snowshoe the Hare. There were Reddy Fox and Ranger the Coyote and Shadow the Lynx and Hunting Cat and Killer the Marten and Digger the Badger and Forktongue the Snake and Snoop the Weasel and dozens of Flying Enemies. Now I ask you if that wasn't enough to make anyone nervous! And so Tawny Chipmunk had to be very watchful most of the time.

Of course there was one nice thing about going to Little River after Pussy Willow Buds. You see, Reddy Fox and Ranger the Coyote and other of the Furry Enemies were not bold while the Laughing Yellow Sun was shining. Forktongue the Snake was still asleep and waiting for warmer weather, and many of the Flying Enemies were still in the Sunny Southland.

But there was Snoop the Weasel. Snoop was the worst Enemy of all. He hunted during the day as well as at night, and, what is more, if he

found Tawny's Hidden Den, he would go right
into it after Tawny. So Tawny had to make many
Secret Tunnels with doorways so that he could
run out if Snoop came into his Hidden Den.

Tawny Chipmunk started down the side of
High Cliff toward Little Jungle Thicket where
Molly and Peter lived. First he skipped along
among the Tumbled Rock Piles until he was near
enough to run to the shelter of Little Jungle
Thicket.

Tawny had been along there many times, for
he went to the Little Jungle Thicket quite often
to look for Tiny Little Seeds and Tempting Berries and other Goodies. He knew every Tumbled
Rock Pile and Friendly Burrow and Hiding Place
along the way.

Tawny Chipmunk hopped up on a large rock
in Little Jungle Thicket and looked around. Before he went on, he wanted to be quite sure that
no Enemy was near.

Suddenly he saw a little streak of brownish-
white fur scooting along on the ground. At first
he thought it was Molly, until he saw Molly sitting
by a Stubby Little Bush. You see, Snoop was beginning to shed his white winter coat and grow a
brown one so he would have it when the Balmy
Summer Days came. That was why he was

neither white nor brown when Tawny saw him.

Tawny wondered what he should do. There was Snoop the Weasel sneaking up to catch Molly; and Molly would not see him until it would be too late to run away. Tawny knew that if he warned Molly, then Snoop would come and catch him. Of course it would not help any if Tawny climbed a tree, for Snoop could climb right up there himself. And if Tawny ran, then Snoop would follow his Scratchy Little Tracks with his keen nose.

Then Tawny Chipmunk thought of a plan; and what do you suppose it was? Down from the rock he dropped and sneaked away until he was at a safe distance.

"Chip-chip-chip-chip," he barked as loud as he could; "I see Snoop the Weasel." And then how he did run toward the Grand Old House!

He knew that Snoop the Weasel would be afraid to follow him there, for Nero the Hound would catch him. And Bud never let Nero bother Tawny Chipmunk.

CHAPTER 29

Miner the Mole Goes Exploring

IT was an exciting night for Miner the Mole when he went exploring in the Green Meadow. The Green Meadow was not yet green, for the weather had not been warm enough to awaken the Tender Grass Shoots. But it would not be long until they would start to peep through the ground. Then what a feast Molly and Peter would have!

But Miner the Mole did not care whether the Green Meadow was green or not. He did not eat Tender Grass Shoots. What Miner liked to eat was Wriggly Earthworms and Plump Grubs and such things as that. He liked to eat the same things that Barney the Shrew ate.

Miner the Mole looked something like Satchelface the Pocket Gopher, but they were not related. While Miner ate Wriggly Earthworms and Plump Grubs, Satchelface the Pocket Gopher ate Tender Grass Shoots and Tempting Kernels and other vegetable food.

It had been a long time since Miner the Mole had gone exploring in the Green Meadow. You

(177)

Miner the Mole had worked under the ground in the
darkness so much that his eyes were almost useless.

see, the ground had been frozen so hard that Miner
could not dig new Secret Little Tunnels along the
top of it in search of Wriggly Earthworms. When
Old Man Winter came, the Wriggly Earthworms
had curled up in bunches and gone to sleep deep
under the ground.

After the Fleecy Snow left, it was not long until
the ground began to get soft again. Warmer and
warmer grew the days until one night Miner the
Mole discovered that the ground was no longer
frozen around his Secret Tunnels. And that was
when he decided to go exploring.

Now, although the days were growing warmer,
still the nights were cold. Sometimes before the
Laughing Yellow Sun came out to warm the earth,

the top of the ground would be frozen again. So Miner thought that if he wanted to go exploring he had better start early. It would never do to wait until the ground started to freeze.

It was strange why Miner preferred to work at night, but he did. Perhaps it was that in the daytime the light hurt his eyes if he came too near the surface. Miner had worked under the ground in the darkness so much that his eyes were almost useless. About all they were good for was to tell him the difference between day and night.

That is the way it is with us. If we do not exercise our bodies we become weak. If we do not use our minds we forget what we have already learned. And if we do not use our Christian experience toward helping others to be better we soon grow indifferent ourselves.

If Miner the Mole ever had good eyes that could see, he certainly did not use them enough to keep them good. No, sir; they were only little specks under the skin.

But Miner was a great worker even though he wanted to work in his own way. He worked almost all the time. That was why he decided to go exploring as soon as he found that the ground was soft enough.

Miner had to keep at work or he would have

had nothing to eat. He could not see to catch anything aboveground; and he could not expect to find anything underground unless he worked for it. Yes, Miner worked for all he got.

Perhaps another reason why Miner liked to work at night was that then the Wriggly Earthworms were near the surface. Miner would go scooting along just under the ground and pushing up a Crooked Little Ridge everywhere he went.

Now it happened that about the time Miner the Mole started out to make some new Crooked Little Ridges, Spot the Skunk decided he would go for a stroll.

"What a nice warm night this is!" he said, as he left his home under the Granary near the Rambling Old Barn. "I wonder if I would find Miner the Mole at work in the Green Meadow tonight." And away he went with his funny little gallop before Nero the Hound could see him.

Spot the Skunk had been living under the Granary during the Cold-Cold Days, where he could hunt for Whiskers the Mouse. But Spot had been thinking that when Jolly Spring came, he would move into a Friendly Burrow somewhere.

Of course you know that Spot the Skunk was a small cousin of Mephitis the Skunk. Some peo-

ple called him Spot the Civet, but he was not a
civet at all, for Mr. Civet Cat lived in the Old
World. Spot was a cousin of Snoop the Weasel,
but he was a gentleman when compared with
Snoop. Both Spot and Snoop could climb trees,
but Mephitis was rather clumsy.

The most dangerous thing about Spot and Mephitis was the Strong Odor that they sprayed upon
anyone who dared to trouble them. Even Nero
the Hound knew better than to get too near. You
could tell that Spot was always ready to defend
himself, because he carried his tail partly up. Then
if anyone came close, up it would go over his back
as a warning.

Down through the Green Meadow went Spot,

"What a nice warm night this is!" said Spot
as he decided to go for a stroll.

stopping now and then to sniff in a Friendly Burrow or to scratch in the soft ground. Spot was not at all particular what he ate, and during the Cold-Cold Days he had not been able to do much hunting for Plump Grubs and such things. But, oh, he did make life miserable for Whiskers the Mouse and his friends! Spot the Skunk could catch more mice than Hunting Cat could.

Suddenly, as Spot was hopping along in the Green Meadow, he noticed a Crooked Little Ridge rising out of the ground. It looked fresh to Spot.

"Sniff, sniff," he went, along the Crooked Little Ridge; "Miner the Mole must be working around here somewhere."

Now Spot the Skunk would almost surely have caught Miner the Mole if something else had not happened right then. Out of the Tangled Grasses came Mephitis the Skunk sniffing along at that Crooked Little Ridge. It would never have done for Spot and Mephitis to spray each other with their Strong Odor, for one could have done that fully as well as the other. So they turned away and went in opposite directions to hunt some other place.

CHAPTER 30

"It's Spring! It's Spring!"

I T was a nice, warm morning in March on the
Old Homestead. Down along Little River
the Pussy Willows were covered with Silky Little
Buds, and overhead the Laughing Yellow Sun was
smiling down in a way that would warm the cold
ground and start the Tender Grass Shoots to
peeping through.

Over in the Black Forest, Growler the Bear had
awakened after sleeping all winter, and had left his
Warm Dark Cave. He was hunting Dried Berries and Dry Grass to eat to start his lazy stomach
to working. Growler did not care to walk much
in search of food until his tender feet became
tough. They were peeling on the bottom after
not using them for such a long time.

Of course Paddletail the Beaver was very busy
at night, fixing his High Dam and cutting Soft
Poplar Trees. Danny Muskrat and Mrs. Muskrat
could dig in the Oozy Mud all they wanted to
after Sweet Cattail Stalks and Juicy Water Bulbs.
Snowshoe the Hare was changing his white winter coat for a grayish tan one, so he could hide

easier when there was no Fleecy Snow on the ground.

Drummer the Grouse had even tried out his Favorite Drumming Log a few times, perhaps to get in practice. And, oh, how happy Lutra the Otter was since he could play Slide and go fishing in the Wildwood Pond without the Glassy Ice bothering!

Lightfoot the Deer was back in the Big Jungle Thicket where there were many Savory Twigs to eat. He was not so afraid of Sneak the Cougar after the Fleecy Snow left.

Trailer the Mink and Billy Coon spent many hours in the Weird Darkness hunting Pinchtoe the Crawfish and other Favorite Food around the Duck Pond and along Little River.

High overhead there was a loud "Honk, honk!" as Honker the Goose sailed over the Old Homestead on his way to his summer home in the Land of Cool Breezes. Out by the Rambling Old Barn, Old Cluck was singing her best spring song. Down in the Wood Lot, Chatterer the Red Squirrel was making a great fuss about nothing. Over on the side of High Cliff, Johnny Chuck lazed around all day and let the Bright Little Sunbeams warm his broad back—that is, when he wasn't eating. Johnny Chuck had not eaten anything all winter, so he had to make up for it now. It seemed as if he never would get enough. How good it was to have spring again!

Virginia Opossum and Mephitis the Skunk and Digger the Badger and Spot the Skunk could all take long strolls at night without the weather's interfering; none of them liked to be out when the night was very cold.

Then there were Molly and Peter Cottontail. How happy they were as the days grew warmer and warmer! They knew that soon the Tender Grass Shoots would be springing out of the ground; and then what a feast they would have! Of course the Dried Clover Leaves, which Bud had brought to them during Wintry Weather, had tasted good; but nothing was quite so delicious as Tender Green Things.

Loxia the Crossbill and Snowy the Bunting and Blue Darter the Goshawk had returned to their homes in the Far North, where they were never too warm.

Over in the Hedgerow along the Apple Orchard, Bobby White whistled his name, "Bob White, Bob-by White," and down in the Green Meadow, which would soon be really green, Ringneck the Pheasant flapped his wings and crowed.

Jim Crow and his undesirable cousins, Tattler

Mr. Bluebird was sitting on the
Nesting Box that Bud had made for him the year before.

the Jay and Pesty the Magpie, were noisier than usual as the days grew longer.

And those three pirates, Shaggy the Wolf and Ranger the Coyote and Reddy Fox, were busy as usual, roaming across the Broad Prairie and through Wildwood Lanes and sneaking through Jungle Thickets, trying to find something to pounce on.

It was an interesting time for all the Wild Creatures on the Old Homestead when the Wintry Weather was past. Of course there would be many more Stormy Days, for it was the time of year when Old Man Winter and Jolly Spring were having an argument about who was running the weather. But it would not be long until Old Man

Winter would go back to the Land of Ice and let Jolly Spring have his way.

And now what do you suppose the Smiths were doing? Well, sir, they were as busy as they could be. You see, it was almost time for Mr. Smith to begin to plow the Fresh Earth Fields and plant them with Tiny Little Seeds. So he was sharpening his plow and doing the other things that he would be too busy to do after he started to plow.

Mrs. Smith was busy with her spring house cleaning so she would have it finished before it was time to plant garden and care for many, many Chicklets, for it would not be long until Old Cluck would decide it was time to sit on some eggs and hatch them.

And then there were Bud and Mary. It kept them busy with their studies and doing their chores. School would not be out for two months, and that was a long time to stay indoors when everything was getting to be so pleasant outside.

"I tell you," said Bud, as they started to school that pleasant March morning, "Old Man Winter is almost whipped. It will not be long until he will have to go to the Far North and hide."

"And then how glad I shall be!" exclaimed Mary.

As Bud and Mary hurried down the Red Stone

Walk toward the front gate, they heard a familiar voice. It was one that they had not heard since Old Man Winter had come and had driven many of their Feathered Friends away to the Sunny Southland.

When Bud and Mary looked up, whom do you suppose they saw? Why, Mr. Bluebird, of course, and he was sitting on the Nesting Box that Bud had made for him and put in the front yard the year before.

"It's spring! it's spring!" said both the children at once, and then they ran back to tell Mother Smith.

They knew that when Mr. Bluebird came back, it would not be long until Jolly Spring would drive Old Man Winter far away from the Old Homestead.